Operations Management
for Healthcare Organizations

Stefano Villa

Operations Management for Healthcare Organizations

Theory, Models and Tools

 Routledge
Taylor & Francis Group
LONDON AND NEW YORK

 G. Giappichelli Editore

First published 2022
by Routledge
2 Park Square, Milton Park, Abingdon, Oxon OX14 4RN

and by Routledge
605 Third Avenue, New York, NY 10158

Routledge is an imprint of the Taylor & Francis Group, an informa business

British Library Cataloguing-in-Publication Data
A catalogue record for this book is available from the British Library

Library of Congress Cataloging-in-Publication Data
A catalogue record for this book has been requested

ISBN: 978-1-032-12959-4 (hbk-Routledge)
ISBN: 978-1-003-22702-1 (ebk-Routledge)
ISBN: 978-1-032-12958-7 (pbk-Routledge)
ISBN: 978-88-921-3967-1 (hbk-Giappichelli)
ISBN: 978-88-921-9655-1 (ebk-Giappichelli)

Typeset in Simoncini Garamond
by G. Giappichelli Editore, Turin, Italy

Università Cattolica del Sacro Cuore contributed to the funding of this research project and its publication.

The manuscript has been subjected to a peer review process prior to publication.

Published by Giappichelli Editore s.r.l. – Torino
June 2021

To my family because, in the end, what really matters is love …
To Francesca for the daily emotions and support
To Pietro ("lo zio") for your attentions
To Andrea for your slight but profound smiles
To Ale for your magic hugs

Within this book there is the support of different important persons in particular my mum and dad, my brother and his fantastic family, Anna and all my other relatives and, finally, all my dear friends ... I cannot mention here all of them, but I promise to all of you a copy of the book with a special dedication. However, a special thanks goes to my friend Zanga for the precious work of language editing.

Finally, the reflections, insights and evidence contained in the book are the results of many years of teaching and research at ALTEMS (*Alta Scuola in Economia e Management dei Sistemi Sanitari*), CERISMAS (*Centro di Ricerche e Studi in Management Sanitario*) and LLP (*Laboratorio Logistica del Paziente*) at Univesità Cattolica del Sacro Cuore... in this sense a special thanks goes, first, to all the colleagues I have worked with but also to all students and executive participants who have played a pivotal role in the framing of the final version of this text.

CONTENTS

LIST OF FIGURES AND TABLES

Figures

Tables

Chapter one

page

INTRODUCTION

Elio Borgonovi [1]

During the 70's of the last century, the Dean at SDA Bocconi School of Management suggested me to design and run programs for Healthcare management, in the belief that: "... *This is not going to be difficult, because functions such as strategy, planning, programming, budgeting, financial and management accounting, organization and HR management, finance, communication, marketing, information system and decision making are based on common knowledge and general skills and can be applied in any complex organization, private or public, manufacturing or service ...*".

My answer was always "... *You are half right and half wrong, half right because knowledge about all these functions you mention are a basic requirement. Half wrong because if we do not know the operations of a specific sector of activity, we cannot help participants to learn how to properly use management theory, methods, techniques, and tools. To be able to teach we need to do research and understand that health services are different from other services. Health services are related to life, death, suffering, and professionals have a complete autonomy and responsibility for prevention, diagnosis, cure, treat and rehabilitation ...*".

Stefano Villa, academically, has grown with a "SDA culture" that has provided the basis and framework of this book. Operations is his field of specialization which he approaches with a system-wide perspective taking into consideration the whole healthcare chain (hospital, diagnosis center, primary and intermediate care and other settings) with the final goal of improving the patient well-being (value based healthcare approach).

Appropriateness and effectiveness can be guaranteed only if operations are well managed.

To use Henry Fayol's definition of management, low efficient operations generate low levels of output and bad outcomes. Unfortunately, many health professionals, in the past and also today, have worked in the belief that the quality of healthcare delivery is related to their own clinical knowledge, expertise and their ethical approach to the patient. Clearly, such attitude is not enough because in complex organizations made up of

---

[1] President of CERGAS (Research Center in Health and Social Care Management) and senior Professor at Department of Social and Political Sciences, Bocconi University.

dozens of units, hundreds and sometimes thousands of doctors, nurses, and other health professional and administrative staffs, processing of diagnosis activities, medical and surgical treatments need to be coordinated. Moreover, acquisition, distribution to unit and use of healthcare materials and technology must be aligned with nursing and clinical activities.

A third reason why focus on operations is critical has to do with the relation between "to know" (theory), "to know how to do" (methods) and "to know how to get things done" (practice).

Vision, mission, strategy, plans do not generate a health pattern for patient, they need execution, that means acting on operations. On the other hand, the analysis of weaknesses in the design and execution of operations can stimulate the introduction of programming, planning, organizational change, people motivation and other innovative processing in hospitals and in other healthcare delivery organizations.

Top and middle managers must be aware that every innovation must undergo an *ex ante* analysis of operations and an ex post evaluation of the actual impact on patients' health.

In this book Stefano Villa draws on his previous researches and teaching experiences. The readers can find solid and rigorous scientific approach and cases that, from one hand, provide a clarification of the implication of theory and, from the other hand, can be used as teaching material.

Another peculiarity of the book, that should be underlined, it is not rooted in the rational choice framework (maximization/optimization) but in an institutional approach that pursues the rationalization of operations within the specific condition (often constrains) of the institution.

In designing operations management change strategies, it is critical to consider all the other relevant organization's elements such as the culture and motivations of people, the features of the building, availability of technology and the actual investment opportunities.

Furthermore, it is a nonsense, an abstract optimization of operations, not considering patients' perceptions and expectations.

Thus, Stefano Villa's book can be included in the socioeconomic system framework rather than in the contingency approach. Operations analysis and improvement are proposed not with the prospective of sub-optimization of this function, but in the prospective of understanding interdependence with the other components of an organization.

Finally, the last key element that qualifies the book is the dynamic approach. Operational system must be continuously adapted to scientific knowledge developement, technology innovation, people competences and motivation, delivery patterns (from cure to care, patient treatment, continuous care model, care networks, value based healthcare etc.).

Lastly, a comment on the structure of the book.

In the first chapter, there is a presentation of main theories of operations, to clarify the meaning of different terms, the differences between operation issue in manufacturing and services companies, especially in health care system.

In the second chapter, the patient flows are analyzed from admission to operating rooms, to discharge. Analytical content and implementation are provided.

The third chapter is dedicated to the supply chain of the materials. It focuses on the relation between external condition and internal processing of materials.

In the fourth chapter, methodologies and tools to manage operations are analyzed in more details. As already mentioned, in every chapter some case studies, from different countries, are included and they add a real international flavor to the book.

Milano – march, 26 2021

Chapter 1
OPERATIONS MANAGEMENT IN HEALTHCARE: WHY, WHAT AND HOW?

1.1. Health care management past, present and future

In order to fully understand the current evolution of the Operations Function within healthcare delivery organizations it is necessary to discuss a little about the evolution of management in the public and healthcare sector.

In the late eighties and early nineties public sector all around the world was invested by the so-called New Public Management (NPM) movement that, basically, argued for the necessity of introducing, in the public sector, organizational models, logics and managerial tools used in the private sector in order to improve the overall performance in the perspective of both efficiency and effectiveness (Dunleavy and Hood, 2009).

In this context, it must be noted that, in most OECD countries, healthcare is still a typical sector of public interest, with the State still playing a relevant role both in the provision (e.g. percentage of publicly owned beds) and in the funding of healthcare.

In the case of healthcare, the concepts of NPM have been implemented along three main dimensions:

1. Increased autonomy and responsibility to each single healthcare delivery organization with increased room for action by general directors;
2. Introduction, as reimbursement scheme, of the DRG (Diagnostic Related Groups) and the development of the so-called quasi-markets aimed to boost competition between providers (public and private);
3. Introduction of managerial models and tools typically used by private organizations such as: (i) budgeting control; (ii) pay-for-performance and (iii) more proactive and less bureaucratic human resources management systems.

This new stream of innovations has invested the traditional organization of healthcare organizations designed around the different clinical specialties (e.g. cardiology, neurology, general surgery and orthopedics). In this type of organizations, clinical directors have complete control over:

1. The use of financial and structural resources;
2. The diagnostic, nursing and clinical treatment of the patients;
3. The control of all the hospital production units (e.g. diagnostics, beds, operating rooms and ambulatories).

In other words, in this type of models there was definitely an abuse of the possessive adjective "my" uttered by the different clinical directors ... "my" beds, "my" operating rooms, "my" patients, "my" nurses and so on.

This old-fashioned model has been slowly torn down by a series of reforms summarized in Table 1.

First at the beginning of nineties, in different countries healthcare delivery organizations have begun to introduce budgeting systems: at the beginning of the year each clinical director was assigned a bucket of resources (structural, financial and human resources) and, at the same time, a set of goals to be achieved along different possible dimensions such as economics, volumes of production, clinical outcome and patient satisfaction.

The limit of this set of reforms is that the budget itself was considered a sort of panacea of all problems and, thereafter, the controller did not take up the challenge/responsibility to look into the production processes thus leaving, in this sense, to each clinical director complete autonomy and control over the actual organization of healthcare delivery processes.

At the beginning of the 2000s in Italy and in many other countries (first UK) scholars, managers and policy makers stressed the importance of controlling decisions and behaviours of clinicians which should have been aligned as much as possible to the evidence-based guidelines and protocols developed, at international level, by scientific associations and government agencies. In this sense, healthcare organizations have started to adopt and implement clinical pathways with the aim of standardizing clinical decisions and behaviours (see Paragraph 1.5).

Finally, in the very last decade, the new models of care tend to overcome the vertical organization based on clinical specialties to move towards more horizontal, flexible, and integrated models where production units are shared across different clinical specialties. To support this new stream of innovations the Operations Management function (the focus of this book) is very much critical.

As it will be explained more in detail in Paragraph 1.7 Operations Management in healthcare has to do with the management and control of production units where healthcare delivery processes take place with the goal of pursuing an efficient, timely and appropriate management of patients and supplies.

The shift to these horizontal and process-based organizations that occurred in the last decade has been triggered by a series of different elements.

Several studies (Aiken et al., 2002; Vissers and Beech, 2005; Litvak et al., 2005; Villa, 2012; Villa et al., 2014) and first-hand experience show that old-fashion specialty-based organizations do not perform satisfactorily under different dimensions likewise efficiency, productivity, timeliness and appropriateness.

Secondly, there was a growing distance between the vertical organization and the current change in epidemiology with a growing share of elderly patients, with chronic conditions and co-morbidities that need, by definition, a more holistic and integrated approach.

The call for more flexible production models was also urged by the mounting pressures for a more efficient use of resources in particular concerning beds, nurses, and physicians.

Finally, right when this book is going to press, we are in the middle of a worldwide healthcare emergency due to pandemic COVID-19. This emergency has dramatically outlined the drawbacks of the current fragmented and vertical organization of healthcare delivery organizations and calls for the immediate implementation of concepts and models inspired to Operations Management science such as (i) timelines and flexibility; (ii) multidisciplinary approach; (iii) capacity planning of hospital production units (e.g., Intensive Care Units), (iv) flows' separation and (v) focused hospital[1].

---

[1] A typical solution adopted to deal with the COVID-19 emergency has been the creation of facilities entirely dedicated to the management of COVID patients managed by multidisciplinary teams. This can be considered an example of focused hospital. The model of the focused hospital will be extensively described in Paragraph 4.4 of this book.

Table 1. Phases of innovation in the organization of healthcare production processes.

Phase/Period	Model/Tools	Aim
1. 1990-onwards	Budget/reporting systems	Assign to clinical directors a budget (in terms of financial, structural and human resources) and a specific set of goals.
2. 2000-onwards	Clinical governance Clinical audit Clinical Pathways	Standardize clinical decisions and behaviors following evidence-based guidelines and protocols
3. 2010-onwards	Patient flows logistics Patient-centred hospital care models Focused hospitals Lean management Value-Based Health Care	Overcome the rigid specialty-based organizational model and move towards a more horizontal, flexible and integrated model.

Source: author's elaboration.

The time frames indicated in Table 1 are merely indicative and they represent a sort of rough average. If you just look at the situation of Italy some healthcare organizations are now well into phase 3 while other organizations are still struggling with the introduction of a budgetary system (phase 1). However, the three moments briefly described above can be considered as a sort of timeline for a possible change plan to redesign healthcare delivery processes. For example, before changing the design and structure of productions models (the so-called "hard" part) moving to more innovative models such as lean or focused hospital it is crucial to work with clinicians for the implementation of clinical pathways (which can be considered the software of the organization).

1.2. Process management

The present work has the ambitious goal to illustrate tools and models to implement the OM function in healthcare delivery organizations. Before dealing with this major topic, however, it is important to start explaining the concept of process management; in fact, the OM function builds around the concept of production processes.

Almost all human activities can be represented as a process: eating dinner in a restaurant, assembling an automobile, approving a home mortgage application, and flying between two cities are all examples of processes that take place in real life.

A process is characterized by a

- sequence of activities that that transform inputs into outputs;
- joint measurable output;
- outcome for a given client (that can be, either, internal or external);
- start and ending.

If we consider production processes taking place at organizations of any type, the sequence of activities usually go well beyond the boundaries traced by the organizational structure. In the case of a hospital organization we can think, for example, about the femur fracture process of care; in this case the process cuts across different units and departments such as (i) emergency department; (ii) radiology; (iii) operating room; (iv) orthopaedics, (v) rehabilitation and (vi) ambulatory care.

In healthcare, establishing the start and end of a given process is not such a straightforward task in fact, the interdependency between acute care, post-acute care and primary care has become increasingly tighter. Furthermore, in the case of chronic conditions the process of care tends to be endless.

In order to successfully managing processes, it is important to consider the special characteristics of healthcare production processes and the public status of many healthcare institutions. In this paragraph we focus on these specificities and outline the possible constrains in process re-engineering projects.

Quality of healthcare processes
Throughout this text, we support the idea that process management and engineering should have, as a final goal, the improvement of quality of care provided to patients. In particular, we refer to the concept of quality as keenly detailed in the report issued by IOM (2001) (p. 37) where the authors have identified six different dimensions for quality improvement:

1. Safety
   Avoiding injuries to patients from the care that is intended to help them.
2. Effectiveness
   Providing evidence-base care capable of solving patient problems avoiding underuse and overuse.
3. Patient-centeredness
   Encompassing, in the provision of care, qualities of compassion, empathy, and responsiveness to the needs, values, and expressed preferences of the individual patient.

4. Timeliness

Reducing waits and sometimes harmful delays for both those who receive and those who give care.

5. Efficiency

Improving the ratio between inputs (resources used) and output (results produced) avoiding waste such as waste of equipment, supplies, ideas, and energy.

6. Equity

Providing care that does not vary in quality because of personal characteristics such as gender, ethnicity, geographic location, and socioeconomic status.

1.3. Specificities of healthcare production processes

At least, five aspects make healthcare production processes unique and different from any other production process in other industries, particularly:

1. Simultaneity between production and consumption;
2. High levels of variability;
3. Management of human lives;
4. Variety of processes and supplies;
5. Professional autonomy.

1. *Simultaneity between production and consumption*

In the case of healthcare, production and consumption occur simultaneously; patient and healthcare professionals need to be present at the same time in the same physical space. This circumstance implies that healthcare delivery organizations need to have the production capacity ready at any time even though the actual production delivery will occur only with the presence of the patient.

It must be said that, with the current technology (e.g. telemedicine) the patient does not need to physically show up at the physician's office but he/she can be virtually present: the recent COVID-19 pandemic has, for example, shown the effectiveness of virtual solutions such as the tele consultation or the tele rehabilitation.

In any case, this specificity implies, for healthcare managers, a double challenge: guaranteeing a certain level of flexibility in the design of production processes and reducing, wherever possible, the fluctuations in the services' demand.

2. *High levels of variability*

Healthcare is subject to three different sources of variability (Litvak and Long, 2000, Noon et al., 2003):

(i)   clinical variability linked to the presence of different diseases, severity levels and responses to therapy;
(ii) demand variability due to the unpredictability of certain typologies of patient flows (e.g., emergency department flows);
(iii) professionals' variability due to different behaviors, approaches, preferences and different levels of ability.

The presence of this variability deeply influences strategic decisions about the level of production capacity and the demand's planning.

As it will be extensively detailed in the Paragraph (1.5), it is important to identify that part of variability (the so-called artificial variability) which can be eliminated because linked to organizational problems or misbehaviors.

3. *Management of human lives*

Managing healthcare production processes is particularly challenging since we are dealing with human lives. For example, a possible stock out (namely the lack of supplies) might have very serious implications if we are talking about life-saving medicines. In this specific case, in fact, an inventory shortage implies the loss of lives and, consequently, the cost of the stock out is much higher than the costs of stocking excess inventory (Mazzocato, 2007).

As better outlined in Paragraph 3.1, exactly for these reasons, JIT models are less common within healthcare delivery organizations.

Secondly, mistakes in the design and execution of healthcare delivery processes such as operating rooms' scheduling or the distribution of medicines to the wards can cause direct harm to patients with possible dramatic events[2].

4. *Variety of processes and supplies*

Within the healthcare sector there is a wide variety of production processes taking place; for example, production processes in units such as ICU (Intensive Care Unit) or ED (Emergency Department) display completely different managerial challenges compared to the delivery of care in other settings such as rehabilitation or ambulatory care.

---

[2] Think, for example, to the case of over-dosage during chemiotherapy. In some cases, this logistical error has broght the death of the patient (Bohmer and Winslow, 1999).

This circumstance implies the need to integrate different competences and different healthcare professionals.

Furthermore, different types of supplies and technologies call for different managerial and organizational models. For example, drugs' management requires specific competences and particular attention for example to the level of stock's temperature and to the expiration date (Villa, 2012).

Finally, both technology and supplies are subject to a constant flow of innovation (Jarret, 2006) which has proved to be above the average when compared with other industries.

5. Professional autonomy

The implementation of change strategies is, finally, more difficult in the healthcare arena because of the traditional resistance and resilience mounted by clinicians.

As outlined by Ackroyd et al. (1989, p. 606), it is possible that senior doctors with leadership positions will adopt a 'custodial orientation': a form of management practice governed largely by professional interests and primarily focused on maintaining the status quo (as defined by the professional community).

In any case, clinical professionals often seem reluctant to respect organizational rules and procedures because they claim that their attention is devoted to patient management rather than to organizational performance and further they identify product standardization as jeopardizing the quality and personalization of treatment (Lega et al., 2013).

In some instances, there is no dialogue at all between managers and clinicians who, sometimes, even perceive the all-organizational machine as a useless system that prevent them to do their job in a proper and timely manner.

This lack of communication and integration between healthcare professionals and those who manage operations is often the cause of the failure of effective change plans in this area.

Because the education of clinicians is founded on science and they, therefore, tend to respond favorably to scientific, fact-based justifications for proposed changes (Freidson, 1988), one way to overcome this problem could be providing clinicians with empirical evidence showing how organizational and operational redesign will streamline processes, improve outcomes, and reduce expenses without lowering levels of clinical effectiveness.

In this perspective, the challenge for healthcare managers is to keep guaranteeing highs standards of service with the main goal to ease healthcare professionals' activity saving time that could be more effectively dedicated to patients' care.

Finally, it must be noted that in a growing number of cases, doctors need also to accomplish teaching and research commitments. This element further influences the design and execution of healthcare production processes. For example, the OR scheduling needs to consider that, in some cases, the time of senior surgeons is dedicated to the training of junior staff while, sometimes, the daily beds' turns are delayed because of the time dedicated to the training of junior fellows.

1.4. Specificities of public sector

In the vast majority of developed countries, a significant part of healthcare delivery organizations is publicly owned[3]. Managing public organizations is different for several aspects (Boyne, 2002, Borgonovi, 2005, Lega et al., 2013):

1. political constraints;
2. different stakeholders and different performance dimensions;
3. bureaucratic model;
4. absence of market price.

1. Political constraints
Political dynamics result in frequent policy changes and the imposition of short-term horizons on public managers. Furthermore, politics is characterized by ambiguity, which is an asset in building and maintaining consensus. Clear goals may well prove unacceptable to some members of a political coalition. As a result, strategic goals tend to be fuzzy and to change frequently. Developing sound long-term operations strategies and innovation projects is therefore more difficult in this context (Zanjirani et al., 2009).

2. Different stakeholders and different performance dimensions
Public organizations face a variety of stakeholders who place demands and constraints on their managers. The presence of different stakeholders (e.g. taxpayers and recipients of services, industrial groups or patients' associations) requires from public organizations to pursue different and sometimes conflicting objectives.

Furthermore, it has frequently been argued that public agencies have distinctive goals, such as ethics, equity or accountability that do not exist in

---

[3] Furthermore, it must be noted that part of the private sector is "no-profit" with mission, goals and organizational models very similar to the public sector. Finally, the all-healthcare sector is deeply regulated with a significant role of the state in the funding systems.

the private sector (Flynn, 2007). However, as noted by several important authors (Moore, 2000, Borgonovi, 2001), the institutional mission of public organizations requires that they meet stakeholders' expectations. All of these broad considerations have a direct and significant impact on operations strategies and innovation projects within the public sector and may require the evaluation of broader dimensions which are typically related to the achievement of public interest goals and that can affect an organization's overall performance.

In the design and planning of hospital productions assets (e.g. operating rooms or emergency departments), considerations about efficiency and productivity should be balanced with the need to guarantee access to care (even in remote and rural areas) and effective response in case of emergencies where timeliness and responsiveness are very much critical.

The current COVID-19 pandemic has shown that, in some cases, the excessive focus on efficiency and productivity has brought to situations where hospitals have been completely incapable to manage, from the very beginning, the peak of activities. In the case of healthcare, the trade-off between flexibility and efficiency needs to be managed carefully. For example, in the case of management of ICUs (the shortage of this type of beds has been highly debated in the current healthcare crisis), the operational goal should be to have a certain percentage of beds always available to accommodate emergency cases and NOT to reach a certain level of saturation.

Another example, in this sense, is the fact that governments often use procurement as a tool to promote a variety of important, broader public policy objectives (Arrowsmith, 1995, Harland et al., 2007) such as economic goals, social goals, and environmental goals and, in some cases, these goals might be in conflict.

In the case of logistics, outsourcing strategies, justified by the aim of pursuing efficiency, raise issues of equality and ethics when employees cease to be civil servants and become employees of a private external contractor (Moschuri and Kondylis, 2006, Bensa et al., 2010).

3. Bureaucratic model
Public organizations are often designed and structured around the principles of the bureaucratic model. Public sector organizations have more formal, less flexible and more risk-averse decision-making procedures than their counterparts in the private sector (Farnham and Horton 1996, Bozeman and Kingsley, 1998).

For example, public contracts are often awarded following rules and principles that are intended to ensure equal supplier treatment, nondiscrimination, and transparency and to reduce the risk of corruption. In addition, the use of spaces and all the scheduling processes need to respect different rules and procedures. In this sense, as outlined by Moore (Moore, 1995), in the case of publicly owned organizations often the value added has nothing to do with the actual result accomplished, but it is linked to the way the process itself is designed and executed. In this case, the compliance to laws and regulations, in the execution of the procurement process, is essential in order to accomplish relevant public goals (such as equity, accountability and legality).

In Chapter 1.10 we have included the only non-healthcare related case "Reengineering public sector production: the case of Boston Housing Authority" with the goal of highlighting the specificities of public organizations that limit possible OM change plans. In public housing, a strategic process is evidently the tenant's selection process: in this case, the design of the process represents a key value driver to achieve important public goal such as equity, transparency, and non-discrimination.

The same concept can be applied in the case of management of waiting lists or in the pre-recovery process: the respect of clear and objective rules and procedures is an essential ingredient to achieve equity of access guaranteeing priority to the most severe clinical cases regardless the type of admission (e.g. private vs. public patients).

It must be noted, however, that the respect of the bureaucratic model may reduce efficiency and increase the overall throughput time of the production process (Doerner and Reiman, 2007). Furthermore, some rules and procedures do not make sense, they are the result of previous practices, and routines that should be eliminated since they represent a useless waste of time.

4. Absence of a market price
In the case of many public services, the price – at the point of access – is almost null; this circumstance introduces a problem of rationing the demand through systems such as waiting lists, waiting time or objective priority systems (e.g. color codes in the ED triage system). These considerations confirm previous findings on public healthcare delivery organizations where capacity is not demand-led; rather, public services organizations meet as much demand as their resources will allow (Walley, 2013).

Specificities vs defects of public organizations

It is worth, in this context, to outline a difference between the four elements mentioned before that represent intrinsic specificities that physiologically influence the behavior of public managers and ancestral pathological drawbacks that traditionally plague efficiency and functionality of public institutions such as:

(i)   lack of a culture of performance measurement and management;
(ii) forms of nepotism in the human resources' management practices;
(iii) little incentive for change and innovation;
(iv) mere respect of the rules with no attention to the actual outcome achieved.

The difference might appear subtle but it is in reality very much relevant; in fact, while the specificities illustrated in the previous session cannot be removed and, somehow, represent the institutional framework that limits the room of action for public managers, the aforementioned defects should be eliminated to move to the next phase of reengineering of public production processes.

Despite these considerations, it must be outlined that there are some elements that make innovation easier in the public sector compared to the private one, particularly:

(1) Public organizations are expected to collaborate and to share their knowledge and practices.
    Therefore, collaborative purchasing and network creation should be stronger within these organisations (Schotanus and Telgen, 2007).
(2) Public organizations can push directly (through specific norms) or indirectly (through moral suasion) private sector organizations in participating in innovative projects (Borgonovi, 2005, Dimitri et al., 2006).
(3) Public organizations, unlike private companies, are typically more willing to introduce drastic changes because they do not fear losing their market share and cannot file for bankruptcy (Borgonovi, 2005).

1.5. Managing variability in healthcare delivery organizations

If we refer to the vast literature about process management (McLaughlin, 1996; Chase et al., 2006; Martone, 2007; Villa, 2012), a key driver for improvement is represented by standardization.

Standardization means that all activities within a certain organization – regardless of who is in charge of the process in that precise moment or the specific location where the process takes place – are performed in exactly the same way following specific procedures and guidelines.

It is, at this point, useful to understand whether standardization is an effective and workable strategy even for healthcare delivery organizations.

McCarthy (2007) in his highly cited article in the *Lancet* quotes Gary Kaplan, Chief Executive Officer of Virginia Mason Medical Center, that, after a visit to a Toyota production plan, wonders

> *"how was that possible: you can create products with no defects; you can have exactly what you need when you need it – and no more and no less – and have that happen every single time. It was the antithesis of what you see in health care."*

Standardization strategies in healthcare sector need to take into account different specific aspects. First, as already mentioned, there are, at least, three different sources of variability: (i) clinical; (ii) professional and (iii) flows. Secondly and most importantly, there are two different sources of variability: (i) natural variability and (ii) artificial variability.

Natural Variability is linked to the nature of healthcare processes, it cannot be eliminated (or even reduced), it can be only optimally managed.

On the contrary, **artificial variability** is caused by dysfunctional processes within the healthcare delivery system and it is, sometimes, linked to misbehaviors and it can be eliminated through managerial interventions.

These two different types of variability require different strategies. As stated before, natural variability cannot be eliminated but managed coherently with organizational mission and goals. On the contrary, artificial variability should be identified and eliminated. As explained in this text, an important task of OM is to chase and eliminate all possible sources of artificial variability.

Table 2 crosses source and type of variability. Clinical variability linked to the clinical condition of patients (pathology, level of severity, co-morbidities) is natural variability. Patients asking for services are different under a clinical, nursing and even social perspective; in this sense, under a managerial perspective, you cannot eliminate this source of variability, but you might redesign the operations system around homogenous categories of patients. This means overcoming the traditional vertical organizational model designed around clinical specialties and moving towards more process-based organization. The following chapters will describe some examples of this type of organizational innovation; in particular the patient-centred model is discussed in Paragraph 2.4 while Paragraph 4.4 presents the focused-factory model.

Table 2. Types and sources of variability.

SOURCE	TYPE	
	Natural (cannot be eliminated but optimally managed)	**Artificial** (can be eliminated through management)
Clinical	X	
Behaviors	X	X
Patient flows (volumes of activity)	X	X

Source: adapted from Villa (2012).

In the case of professionals' variability, we have both types of variability. In fact, for homogenous groups of patients it is possible to standardize the behaviors of healthcare professionals through the implementation of clinical pathways.

A clinical pathway is described as "an optimal sequencing and timing of interventions by physicians, nurses, and other staff for a particular condition, designed to minimize delays and resources utilization and, at the same time, maximize the quality of care".

Of course, the standardization of the clinical decision making process – through the adoption of clinical pathways – is easier with those clinical conditions (think for example to COPD[4] or femur fracture or stroke) where there is unanimous consensus in the scientific community about the best diagnostic and therapeutic treatment.

Clinical pathways identify structures (institutions, facilities, units etc.), care-givers (clinical professionals) and treatment paradigms that intervene at critical points to efficiently treat the patient and achieve a defined outcome in a given healthcare delivery organization. It is a concrete organizational declination of the evidence-based recommendations (clinical guidelines and protocols).[5]

---

[4] COPD: Chronic Obstructive Pulmonary Disease.

[5] The implementation of clinical pathways is not the focus of the current text. For Italian readers good references on these aspects are:

Tozzi V (2004), La gestione per processi in sanità, Mecosan, 50.

Baraghini G., Capelli M., Capponi A., Longo F., Tozzi V., Villa S. (2006) «La gestione per processi per il governo clinico ed il controllo dei rischi: un confronto di metodo tra Aziende Ospedaliere» in Anessi Pessina E., Cantù E. (2006), L'aziendalizzazione della sanità in Italia, Rapporto OASI 2006, Egea, Milano.

De Belvis e Bucci a cura di (2018) "Come organizzare l'assistenza del paziente per percorsi di cura. L'esperienza presso la Fondazione Policlinico Universitario "Agostino Gemelli" Vita e Pensiero.

In this perspective, any variation from the sequence of activities described in the clinical pathway must be considered a type of artificial variability that should be, by definition, identified and eliminated.

It is important, however, to stress that standardization projects, in the healthcare sector, need to be implemented carefully, in fact, some variation in clinical behaviors can be considered natural for at least three different considerations:

(i) it is not always easy to identify homogeneous group of patients;
(ii) standardization is not always a feasible approach especially for those particularly complex clinical conditions and with a low level of agreement on the best diagnostic and treatment paradigm;
(iii) some patients, because of co-morbidities or particular clinical or social conditions, may fall off the pathway.

A couple of examples may help to clarify these concepts.

For example, the case of COPD clinical condition: sound and robust scientific evidence has defined clear rules and algorithms to establish when it is necessary to opt for invasive breathing support. However, non-invasive breathing support can be difficult to apply if the patient is not collaborative enough; in some cases, for example, young children, a more invasive procedure can be the best solution despite the recommendations developed at international level. In this case, we are dealing with a type of variability that can be labelled as natural and, therefore, needs to be accepted and cannot be eliminated.

A second example is the variability of surgical time, considered as the time interval between the first surgical incision and the last stitch[6]. Scientific literature and anecdotal evidence indicate that even for minor procedures (e.g., hernia or cholecystic) we record significant variability within the same surgical team. Is this natural or artificial variability? It is both. It is artificial when the surgeon is not well trained, or he/she does not follow procedure, checklists, or clinical pathways. However, surgical times may differ first because of clinical natural variability on patient side but also because of different attitudes or preferences that can be judged natural if the surgeon is well trained and respects all rules and procedures. If this is the case this type of variability cannot be eliminated but optimally managed; for example, in the weekly OR scheduling we should consider that surgeon XYZ takes, on average, 30 minutes more compared to the other surgeons in the team.

---

[6] For an extensive analysis of Operating Room indicators we refer the reader to paragraph 2.2.

Drawing the line between natural variability and artificial variability is not always easy and straightforward also because clinicians, for training and cultural background, tend to justify their variability as natural making arguments such as ... "*my patients are different, ... my wards admit more complicated patients ... my patients are more elderly ...*" and so on.

As said, a third source of variability depends on patient flows variability. In healthcare, patients do not come on a steady state but they often come randomly with peaks and lows across the hours in a day, the days in a week, the weeks in a month and so on. Even in this case it is, however, critical making a distinction between natural and artificial variability. A typical source of natural variability is represented by the ED (Emergency Department): health care managers, in fact, cannot control the flow of patients who show up at the ED with a stroke, an aneurism or a femur fracture. This natural variability cannot be eliminated but optimally managed through, for example, the activation of maxi emergency plans in case of unexpected peaks in arrivals of patients (because of a pandemic or a terrorist attack or a big cars' accident). Furthermore, often, as analyzed in Paragraph 2.3, ED arrivals present recurrent patterns (e.g. Monday is the busiest day of the week while mid-morning is the busiest time within the day) that could be better managed with a more coherent and appropriate staffing management allocating more ED personnel during these time periods.

In conclusion, when we look at patient flow variability it is important to make a distinction between emergency patients (patient who show up, typically through the ED, without invitation) and elective patients (patients with a scheduled invitation). It is, among this latter group that we can identify different sources of artificial variability such as (i) a bad ORs scheduling with a concentration of procedures in the middle of the week; (ii) a fragmented organization of the pre surgical testing process; (iii) systematic delays in the start of the surgical procedures.

These situations determine a possible deterioration of the overall quality and safety of the care provided to patients. Particularly, as represented in Figure 1, whenever healthcare professionals need to deal with peaks in activity we register problems such as: (i) errors; (ii) long waiting times; (iii) cancelled cases and (iv) burnt-out for healthcare professionals especially nurses; (iv) delay in the discharge process.

The highly cited study conducted by Aiken and colleagues (2012) provides some robust evidence to support these considerations:

- any additional surgical patient assigned to a nurse beyond the ratio 1 nurse to 4 patients determines an increase by 7% of the mortality rate for all patients managed by the same nurse;

– shortage of nurses, used as explicatory variable in a regression model, explains 24% of all sentinel event recorded in a hospital.

On the contrary, whenever we have a low in the volume of activities we are, actually, wasting resources with problems of productivity and efficiency (cfr. Figure 1).

Figure 1. The possible consequences of patient flow variability.

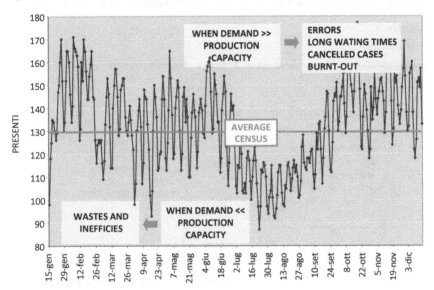

Source: author's elaboration.

The main aim of this paragraph is to stress the importance for healthcare professionals to make a distinction between natural and artificial variability. It is, in fact, very much critical, in the design of OM strategies, to identify and eliminate all the sources of artificial variability and to manage natural variability that, on the contrary, cannot be eliminated (see Table 2).

As already mentioned, drawing the line and making a distinction between natural and artificial variability, it is not easy and straightforward for, at least, three different reasons:

1. some elements (such as the surgical time described above) have both a natural and artificial component;
2. the analysis of variability requires, for healthcare managers, the adoption of new models and techniques partly illustrated throughout the present text;
3. physicians tend to label their variability in decisions and behaviours as "natural", arguing that their own patients and wards are different.

1.6. Process improvement

We have stressed the point that any reengineering project needs to take into account the specific elements that characterize production processes in publicly owned healthcare delivery organizations. As for the methodology to follow in the change projects, we can, on the contrary, easily refer to the general literature (Davenport, 1993; Tozzi, 2004 and Villa, 2012) that identifies four different phases in the process improvement cycle (see Figure 2):

1. analysis;
2. planning;
3. changing;
4. monitoring.

Figure 2. The four phases of a process improvement project.

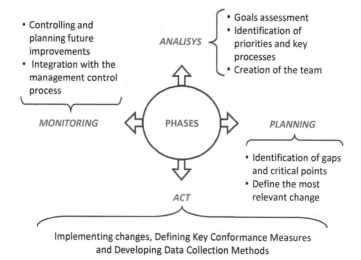

Source: adapted from Villa (2021).

The analysis phase implies four different activities

1. Goal's assessment where it is important to clearly indicate the goals of the change plan;
2. Identification of the boarders of the project in other words which process you want to analyse and, subsequently, improve;
3. Creation of the team in charge to coordinate and lead the change;
4. Process mapping with the goal to represent the current situation of the process ("as is") with a clear and complete representation of actors and activities involved.

In the analysis of the current processes, we should be able to address questions such as:

- What is done and why?
- What is the value of the current activity?

In this initial phase the point is not to mandate what activities should be performed and how, but to understand what is actually done at the moment ("AS IS"); in fact, documenting the process of care delivery is a precondition for making improvements.

As previously mentioned, any process is characterized by a sequence of activities; in the mapping process these activities can be represented at varying levels of granularity. The general principle is to begin by delineating the process at a level of detail that allows to achieve a general understanding of all the important groups of activities and the different actors and organizational units involved. Further, more detailed analyses can be performed at a subsequent time.

To map the processes there are different tools and models. A quite simple but effective tool is represented by the flow chart that crosses actors (on the horizontal axis) and activities (on the vertical axis). In the figure below we represent the main symbols used by this methodology.

Figure 3. Flowchart: most common symbols.

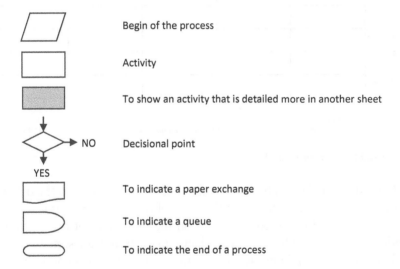

Source: adapted from Villa (2012).

After completing the analysis of the processes under revision, a second phase starts. This will have to do with the <u>planning</u> of the change plan that has the aim to:

- Identify the most relevant gaps and critical points;
- Define the most relevant change drivers[7];
- Formulate a complete and detailed change plan.

The change plan needs to detail the exact timing of the interventions typically across a time span of three years. According to Nicosia (2010) it is important to wisely mix quick and easy projects with a high likelihood of success (the so called quick-wins projects) with mid-long-term projects that require more resources and the support of different organizational units.

However, in the choice of the projects / solutions, a good tool is represented by the so-called focusing matrix (cfr. Figure 4) that crosses two different dimensions: (i) the relevance of the solution suggested that must be interpreted as the concrete capability of solving the problems identified in the analysis phase and (ii) the ease of implementation considering different aspects such as financial resources to invest, competences required, cultural resistance or technological requirements.

Figure 4. Focusing Matrix.

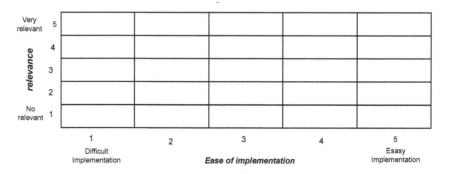

Source: adapted from Villa (2012).

Once the change plan has been defined, it is time to move to the delicate phase of <u>action</u>. Even if this is not the focus of the present text, it is relevant to refer to some relevant contributions on the most relevant organizational conditions to successfully implement change in the healthcare sector.

Borgonovi (1996), in particular, identifies three particular conditions:

---

[7] The next paragraph will provide a description of the drivers for improving operations in healthcare.

1. The willingness to change;
2. The support from the strategic management;
3. The competences to lead the change.

Bodega (2002) remarks how critical it is that change is led by people with enough charisma and leadership skills and with formal strategic roles within the organization.

Another key factor is time; two common mistakes: (i) thinking of having the ability to change complicated processes in few months because, for example, the political mandate of the CEO is about to end or (ii) thinking to rely upon an undefined time. In general, a good time span to change complicated healthcare production processes is approximately two years.

At the end of the improvement cycle, there is the last important phase, monitoring the results accomplished with the changes implemented. This phase is characterized by three main activities:

1. Definition of a sort of a dashboard of indicators capable to validly measure the impact expected with the change plan;
2. Choice of standards to benchmark the results achieved at organizational level;
3. Integration with the information system in order to include these indicators within the planning and control organizational system.

In the following chapters, we will be presenting a possible dashboard of indicators to measure the performance of Operations Management systems for healthcare delivery organizations. In this paragraph, however, we outline some basic characteristics of a good monitoring system.

– The dashboard should contain few indicators; computing indicators is, in fact, costly and time-consuming and it is, therefore, important to focus only on the few most relevant ones.
– Measures need to be reliable, i.e., free of error, and valid, i.e., the indicator needs to be associated with the construct it is supposed to measure.
– Indicators chosen to measure the impact of a given change project should be included in the normal planning and control system and, thus, inserted in the budget of personnel and organizational units.
– Each indicator should then be compared with a standard. Standards can be different: (i) other organizational units operating within the same organization; (ii) other healthcare delivery organizations or even (iii) other industries. In this latter case, it is important to take into account the specificities of public healthcare organizations indicated at the beginning of this chapter.

1.7. Definition and evolution of Operations Management in health-care

General definition

The Operations Management function includes all the activities of planning, management and control of production processes that transform inputs into outputs. In many industries, there is growing awareness that OM is a very critical and strategic function and it represents an essential driver for value creation.

It is important, at this stage of the book, not to make mistakes between different concepts and terminologies.

First of all, Operations Management (OM) is something different from operations research; operations research is not a managerial function but it is a discipline that develops and tests mathematical and statistical models (for example, queuing modelling or simulation or optimization functions) that provide useful information to support many OM decisions. In this book (chapter 4.6) we will provide some basic hints on how to use the queuing model but we won't go into the mathematical details of this type of models.

Secondly, it is important to distinguish the OM function from the production model most popular in a given historical period.

In fact, we have seen, over the years, different production models which have influenced and, somehow, shaped the OM function for example the ford model in the 19th century, later at the beginning of this century the Total Quality Management model and, nowadays the lean model or the focused factory system.

However, a good operations manager should avoid following the fashion of the moment, instead he/she should adopt and implement those models that are more coherent with the organization's mission and the specific nature of the organization's production processes.

As illustrated in the previous Paragraph, before implementing any type of change plan in the production processes, it is important to carry out a complete analysis of the current situation and clearly identify the strategic goals to pursue. Sometimes managers tend to skip this part and they rapidly introduce changes without an actual strategic thinking with the net effect of achieving no improvements at all and, in some cases, even making the situation worse.

As indicated by several authors (Bowman e Fetter, 1957; Chase et al., 2004; Grando et al., 2010; Villa, 2012) any type of OM change plan should:

- develop a performance management system capable of taking into account the specificities of each production system;
- design and implement an operational system coherent with the organization strategic goals;

- adopt a process perspective; in fact optimizing single pieces of the entire organization would lead to suboptimal results or, in some cases, even to a deterioration of the performance of the organization;
- be coherent with the structure of organizational infrastructure[8].

Operations Management in healthcare

In Paragraph 1.2 we have provided a first general definition of process management. In healthcare the so-called "core" or primary processes are represented by all clinical and nursing activities performed to patients to solve specific problems of care. This Paragraph, instead, focuses on the role and areas of responsibility of healthcare Operations Management. It has been quite a few years since I have started my introductory classes on OM in healthcare with a short incident drawn from the book written by Atul Gawande (Gawande, 2007 pp. 6-10):

> By _two o' clock,_ I had finished with the procedures for my patients before her and I was ready too. Then I got a phone call.
> Her case was being delayed, a woman from the OR control desk told me. Why? I asked.
> The recovery room[9] was full. So three operating rooms were unable to bring their patients out, and all further procedures were halted until the recovery room opened up.
> OK. No problem. This happens once in a while. We'll wait.
> By _four o'clock_, however, Magboo still had not been taken in. I called down to the OR desk to find out what was going on. The recovery room had opened up, I was told, but Magboo was getting bumped for a patient with a ruptured aortic aneurysm coming down from the emergency room. The staff would work on getting us another OR.
> I explained the situation to Magboo, lying on her stretcher in the preoperative holding area and apologized. Shouldn't be too much longer, I told her. She was philosophical. What will be will be, she said. She tried to sleep to make the time pass more quickly but kept waking up. Each time she awoke, nothing had changed.
> At _six o'clock_ I called again and spoke to the OR desk manager. They had a room for me, she said, but no nurses. After five o'clock, there are only enough nurses available to cover seventeen of our forty-two operating

---

[8] With the term organizational infrastructure we include both the (i) strategic planning and control system and (ii) organizational structure. The strategic planning and control system encompass the planned system objectives and policies that hospital sets, at different levels, in delivering care and meeting performance goals while organizational structure refers to the formal assignment of roles and functions, the division of work among the different units and all the mechanisms to make the hospital work (Airoldi, Brunetti and Coda 2004).

[9] The Recovery Room is a physical space next to the OR block where patients are brought, immediately after intervention, to wake up.

rooms. And twenty-three cases were going at that moment – he'd already made nurses in four rooms do mandatory overtime could not make any more. There was no way to fit another patient in.

Well, when did he see Magboo going?

"She may not be going at all," he said. After seven, he pointed out, he'd have nurses for only nine rooms; after eleven, he could run at most five. And Magboo was not the only patient waiting. "She will likely have to be cancelled," he said. Cancel her? How could we cancel her?

I went down to the control desk in person. One surgeon was already there ahead of me lobbying the anesthesiologist in charge. A second was yelling into the OR manager's ear on the phone. Each of us wanted an operating room and there would not be enough to go around. A patient had a lung cancer that needed to be removed. Another patient had a mass in his neck that needed to be biopsied. "My case is quick," one surgeon argued. "My patient cannot wait," said another.

Operating rooms were offered for the next day and none of us wanted to take one. We each had other patients already scheduled who would themselves have to be cancelled to make room. And what was to keep this mess from happening all over again tomorrow, anyway?

I tried to make my case for Magboo. She had a breast cancer. It needed to be taken out. This had to happen sooner rather than later. The radioactive tracer, injected more than eight hours ago, was dissipating by the hour. Postponing her operation would mean she would have to undergo a second injection of a radioactive tracer – a doubling of her radiation exposure – just because an OR could not be found for her.

That would be unconscionable, I said.

No one, however, would make any promises.

Virginia Magboo lay waiting, anxious and hungry, in a windowless, silent, white-lit holding area for still two hours more. The minutes ticked, ticked, ticked. At times, in medicine, you feel you are inside a colossal and impossibly complex machine whose gears will turn for you only according to their own arbitrary rhythm.

Magboo asked me if there was any real prospect of her having her operation that night. The likelihood, I said, had become exceedingly small. But I couldn't bring myself to send her home, and I asked her to hang on with me. Then, just before eight o'clock, I got a text message on my pager. "We can bring your patient back to room 29" the display read. Two nurses, it turned out, had seen how backed up the ORs had gotten and, although they could easily have gone home, they volunteered to stay late. "I didn't really have anything else going on anyway," one demurred when I spoke to her. When you make an effort, you find sometimes you are not the only one willing to do so. Eleven minutes after I got the page, Magboo was on the operating table, a sedative going into her arm. Her skin was cleaned. Her body was draped. The breast cancer came out without difficulty. Her lymph nodes proved to be free of metastasis. And she was done. She woke up calmly as we put on the dressing. I saw her gazing upward at the operating light above her.

"The light looks like seashells," she said.

Usually, I use this short story in my introductory classes of healthcare Operations Management to exemplify the relevant impact of this function on the overall quality of healthcare provision. In particular, I ask participants to identify all the quality problems present in the case, referring to the six dimensions of quality issued by the Institute of Medicine (cfr. Paragraph 1.2) and namely:

1. Effectiveness;
2. Safety;
3. Efficiency;
4. Timeliness;
5. Equity;
6. Patient centeredness.

Secondly, I ask the class to randomly list the organizational issues that cause the quality defects. The Table below (Table 3) includes some examples of the results of these (very enlightening) class discussions.

Table 3. Quality defects and organizational problems in the story of Magboo.

Quality Problems	Organizational Sources
Patient centeredness Bad experience for the patient Magboo who had to wait for several hours naked with only the surgical clothing.	Bad ORs scheduling No separation of flows: emergency and elective cases competing for the same resources.
Safety Risk of a second injection of a radioactive tracer	Bad management of nurses' shifts
Nurses forced to do overtime in a stressful environment with increased probabilities of making errors.	Recovery Room possible bottleneck [10] Badly designed ORs' lay-out
Efficiency Payment of the overtime for nurses	Lack of control on key production units such as the operating rooms.
Famous and well-paid surgeon idle for several hours	
Timeliness Patient waiting in front of the OR for more than five hours.	

Source: author's elaboration.

---

[10] A bottleneck is that activity, throughout the whole process, that slows down the rhythm of the entire process.

This short incident shows a case where a series of quality problems are caused not by errors and/or misbehaviours imputable to nurses and physicians, instead, they are the consequence of a badly designed and executed OM system.

In fact, all the organizational issues illustrated in Table 3 point to operational problems such as (i) a badly designed lay-out; (ii) an inadequate scheduling system; (iii) a lack of coordination between elective and emergency flows and (iv) defects in the design and execution of production processes.

This circumstance is proved also by several scientific studies (Litval and Long, 2000; Aiken et al., 2002; Villa, 2012; Villa et al., 2014) that show how often quality of care is put at risk because of factors that have nothing to do with clinical activities. Further real-life aspects may clarify this concept (Villa, 2012):

(i)   patient's admission to the inappropriate setting not because a faulty clinical decision but due to a shortage of beds;
(ii) long waiting time for elective surgical cases;
(iii) delays for the surgical treatment of patients with femur fracture put "on hold" in the ED;
(iv) errors in drugs' logistics that cause situations of over or under dosage.

These few examples show the importance of making a distinction between clinical issues linked to behaviors and decisions made by nurses and physicians and operational aspects linked to decisions about the design and planning of input flows within the production processes.

Given the peculiarity and complexity of healthcare production processes (Cfr. Par. 1.3) we can distinguish two different types of flows: (i) patients and (ii) materials. Consequently, in healthcare, OM includes two different dimensions (cfr. Figure 5):

1. patient flow logistics;
2. supply chain management.

Figure 5. Operations Management in healthcare sector.

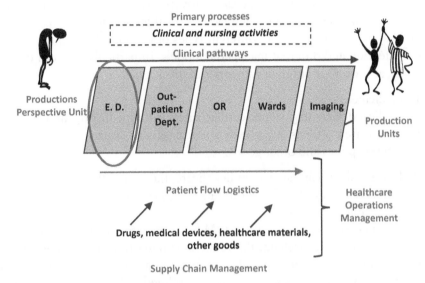

Source: adapted from Villa (2012).

Patient flow logistics has to do with the management of patient physical paths/routes within a healthcare delivery organization from the very first access, to the triage towards the most appropriate setting, until the very end phase of discharge and integration with post-acute care. The focus is the optimization of patient flows throughout all the different production units along the entire healthcare chain. In the case of a hospital, we can identify, at least, five different categories of production units (cfr. Figure 5):

1. Operating Rooms.
2. Emergency Department.
3. Ambulatories.
4. Wards.
5. Imaging departments.

In Paragraph 2.1 we will suggest a specific methodology to analyse hospital patient flow logistics.

Supply Chain Management (SCM), instead, focuses on materials with the goal of ensuring that an efficient and timely flow of materials occurs throughout the production cycle. In reality, the concept of supply chain management has a broader meaning and it includes the relationships with the suppliers (upstream) and the clients (downstream). Chapter 3 is entirely dedicated to illustrate models, change drivers and performance dimensions of SCM. Particularly, in the healthcare sector there will not be a one-fits all SCM system, since there are different types of supplies that require different attention and different managerial models. In particular, we can distinguish, at least, four different categories of inventories:

1. medicines;
2. medical devices (e.g. stents, cardiac valves, orthopedic prosthesis);
3. healthcare materials (e.g. gloves, surgical scissors, gauze);
4. office supplies and other goods.

In general, we can say that, in healthcare, the goal of the OM function is to optimally manage the flow of inputs (supplies and patients) towards the primary clinical processes.

In other words, the role of the OM function is to satisfy, in a timely, efficient and effective fashion, the requests coming from healthcare professionals (doctors and nurses) who, eventually, are the process owners of primary clinical processes. Of course, as outlined in Paragraph 1.5, clinical decisions and behaviours should be, as much as possible, standardized and coherent with protocols and guidelines developed at international level. However, this latter aspect is not responsibility of the OM function but falls within the competences and responsibilities of the clinical governance area.

An example might clarify this concept. The figure below (Figure 6) exemplifies the possible macro pathways for a patient with a diagnosis of colon cancer: (i) medical treatment with chemotherapy; (ii) surgical intervention and (iii) radiotherapy.

In this case, the OM is responsible for aspects such as:

(i)   delays in the diagnostics process;
(ii)   long waiting times for a visit or a surgery;
(iii) shortage of beds in specific settings (e.g. ICU);
(iv) elective cases bumped or postponed because of a bad ORs scheduling;
(v)   scarce utilization of critical production units such as operating rooms or oncological DH.

On the other hand, clinicians should be accountable for the other more clinical aspects such as (i) the wrong decision about the most appropriate treatment (e.g. medical treatment vs. surgical intervention); (ii) mortality rate; (iii) readmission's rate.

In a sense, clinical governance and Operations Management are the two sides of the same coin or, if you prefer, the two opposite buttonholes of the same pullover zip[11]: clinical governance sets the demand, the standard of care that should be appropriate and coherent with international guidelines while OM transforms this demand in efficient, timely and effective production processes. At the same time OM guys that collect first-hand data provide precious information and feedback for monitoring the actual level of appropriateness of care delivered.

In other words, optimizing operations makes sense as far as clinical decisions are appropriate and evidence-based. For example, increasing the efficiency and productivity of ORs is definitely a good thing but we need to make sure that the surgical activity performed is appropriate. Going back, for example, to the case outlined in figure 6 we should address the following question: based on the most recent scientific guidelines, the surgical option is actually better compared to the medical treatment?

Figure 6. The possible macro pathways for a patient with colon cancer.

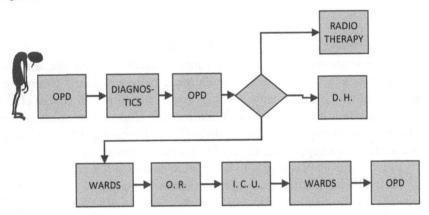

OPD: Outpatient Department
DH: Day Hospital
O.R.: Operating Room
I.C.U.: Intensive Care Units

Source: author's elaboration.

At the very time I have been finalizing this text we are still in the middle of the COVID-19 pandemic: in this context healthcare Operations Management systems are required to deal with three different challenges.

---

[11] This metaphor, I need to admit, is not mine but it is actually a comment by one of the participants at the Master of Science in Healthcare Operations, namely Maurizio Pocaforza, operations manager at Reggio Emilia Local Health Authority.

1. **Responsiveness**

   Addressing the pandemic with timely and flexible production processes capable of dealing with peaks and valleys linked to the virus epidemiological curve.

2. **Resilience**

   Guaranteeing the continuity of care especially for the most critical and fragile part of the population like oncological patients.

3. **Restoration**

   Redesigning the current structure of healthcare production processes building up around what we have learnt during the pandemic.

In this third phase, there will be a lot of room for innovation (think for example about the all-area of digital health) in order to (i) catch up with the backlog of visits and procedures delayed during the pandemic and (ii) to address a completely new set of people's needs. In this scenario, the OM function will play a pivotal role in successfully moving from strategy to practice.

Operations Management and Clinical Governance

The considerations about the colon cancer example, outline the absolute relevance of achieving a positive equilibrium between clinical governance and Operations Management. In other words, the people in charge of the clinical decision-making process should provide clear and complete inputs to operations managers in order to design OM systems capable of efficiently and effectively supporting the all different processes of care.

Few other examples may help better understanding this concept.

As it will be illustrated in more details in Paragraph 2.4, the current trend in the innovation of hospital models is to reorganize wards based on different criteria from the traditional clinical specialty. For example, a patient with breathing problems – traditionally assigned to a respiratory unit – in these models, on the basis of the clinical and nursing complexity, can be alternatively assigned to one of these units: (i) ICU (Intensive Care Unit); (ii) high care; (iii) regular wards or (iv) low care. It is, thus, important to clearly spell out the criteria to get IN and get OUT from these different settings so the OM guys can properly plan the beds' capacity and, therefore, accommodate the right patient to the appropriate setting.

Scientific evidence clearly shows that, in several clinical conditions, timeliness of care does have a direct impact on the clinical outcome of the process of care. In this sense, a very well-known example is the femur fracture case: several studies prove that bringing the patient to the OR within 48 hours has a positive direct impact on a series of clinical outcomes including the effectiveness of the rehabilitation process. Achieving the 48 hours standard requires important interventions in the OM system, like:

- A very timely and efficient triage process at the ED;
- A redesign of OR lay-out in order to have dedicated pathways for urgent cases;
- A careful OR scheduling capable of avoiding overlapping between emergency and elective flows.

A third example is drawn from the oncological care, where we witness a very fast pace of innovations especially regarding the continuous introduction of new drugs. In order to fully reap all the benefits of this stream of innovations, it is necessary to continuously redesign the supply chain management system ensuring an efficient, safe and timely flow of materials, specifically medicines.

Finally, as extensively discussed in Paragraph 4.3, a key feature in the design and implementation of clinical pathways is the multidisciplinary approach. Even in this case, different distinctive features of the OM systems become essential, like:

- shared and multidisciplinary spaces;
- OR scheduling that needs to take into account the necessity of having different professionals around the operating table treating the same patient;
- redesign operational aspects such as (i) organization of medical rounds; (ii) beds' management and (iii) discharge letter.

Throughout all this text, we have extensively illustrated the importance of managing the interdependencies between Operations Management and clinical governance. The OM function plays, in fact, a critical role in supporting primary clinical processes along, at least, four different dimensions:

1. *Appropriateness*
   The clinical and nursing criteria defined to get IN and get OUT the different settings (e.g. ICU or high care) need to be included in the hospital scheduling system particularly, at the two main entries of a hospital: (i) the ED and the (ii) ambulatory.
2. *Timeliness*
   The use of models and techniques of OM (e.g. lean or queueing theory) extensively illustrated in this book represents an important help to streamline and speed processes. Time – in many critical processes of care (e.g. stroke, femur fracture, heart attack – does represent a key element in the overall clinical recovery.

3. *Multidisciplinary Approach*

   The new epidemiological context calls for the creation of multidisciplinary teams and settings. To sustain this new types of organizational models the OM function appears very much critical in the re-design of the healthcare production processes from the phase of admissions, to the organization of medical rounds down to the discharge process.

4. *Flexibility*

   The current COVID-19 pandemic has shown the relevance of setting up highly flexible systems capable of dealing with fluctuations of demand that may be linked with the diffusion of different possible type of virus.

Table 4. Interdependencies between clinical governance and Operations Management.

Critical dimension of primary clinical processes	The role of OM	Impact on quality of care
Appropriateness		
Clear criteria to get IN and get OUT from the different settings	Hospital Capacity Planning System	Appropriateness of the level of care provided to patients.
Timeliness		
Provision of care (e.g. surgical procedure) within certain time standards	The use of models and techniques of OM.	Direct impact on clinical outcome (e.g. recovery after femur fracture)
Multidisciplinary Approach		
Creation of multidisciplinary teams and settings.	Re-design of the healthcare production processes from the phase of admissions, to the organization of medical rounds down to the discharge process.	Several studies have proved a direct link between the multidisciplinary approach and the levels of appropriateness and clinical outcome provided to the patients.
Flexibility		
Capability of dealing with fluctuations of demand linked to emergency situations (e.g. the spread of a virus).	Flexibility in scheduling and capacity planning (e.g. inpatient beds) management	Timely, appropriate and effective care.

Source: author's elaboration.

Evolution of OM function in healthcare

The role of OM begun to get momentum in Italy (but also in other universalistic and public systems such as UK) only at beginning of 2000. Particularly, it was clear how a fragmented specialty-based organization was systematically underperforming with respect to efficiency and productivity dimensions.

In this initial phase, the main aim was to improve efficiency through a more flexible and proactive allocation and management of production assets within, still, a specialty-based organization.

Only, afterwards, at the beginning of 2010 managers and policy makers began to promote innovative programs aims to overcome the traditional specialty based organizational model: the idea was to separate patient flows depending on the intensity of care required by each single patient (cfr. Par. 2.4).

In this very last period, the challenge is to redesign patient flow logistics according to the basic principles of value-based healthcare that sustains the necessity to redesign assets and operational models around clinical conditions such as diabetes or hip replacement proposing a stronger link and connection between Operations Management and clinical governance (cfr. Par. 4.2).

This transition towards organizational models that imply a redesign of operational systems around clinical conditions represents also a step forward in the evolution of the OM function. The rise of this function, in fact, has been typically justified by the need of enhancing efficiency in the attempt to addressing an increasingly growing demand with shrinking resources. However, other dimensions such as timeliness, appropriateness, patient satisfaction should inform the design of healthcare operations.

This change implies a stronger connection between Operations Management and clinical governance with a different role for OM people that should be more involved in the construction and implementation of clinical pathways but also in the design of the overall organization's strategies.

1.8. Logistical Drivers

To improve operations' performance it is possible to act on four different drivers (Bowersox and Closs, 1996; Villa, 2012):

1. Capacity planning;
2. Lay-out and organization of spaces;
3. Design and organization of processes and activities;
4. Information and technological innovation.

We provide, in this Paragraph, a brief explanation of each of these drivers while we refer the reader to the following chapters for more concrete examples about patient flows logistics (Chapter 2) and supply chain management (Chapter 3).

The first driver (*capacity planning*) includes two different dimensions:

on the one, we have the more strategic decisions about the capacity to set-up, in terms of number of beds, operating rooms, diagnostics etcetera and, on the other, tactical decisions on how to use this capacity. In other words, I need, first, to make the hard and strategic decision about the overall number of operating rooms to build and, secondly, I need to decide how to allocate these operating rooms among the different specialties. As previously explained, unlike other industries where it is possible to completely even out workload fluctuations, in the case of healthcare, forecasting and planning actual capacity is definitely more challenging because it is necessary to include the so-called natural variability (cfr. 1.5). However, as it will be extensively explained in chapter two, the delivery of care hides several elements of artificial variability that should be identified and eliminated.

Decisions about *layout and organization of spaces* do play a role in the management of healthcare operations. It must, first, be outlined that, in the last years in Europe we have witnessed to important projects of redesign of hospital structures aimed at separating hospital wards from supporting services such as laboratories, operating rooms and diagnostics (Colombo and Mauri, 2010).

In my previous book (Villa, 2012: 102-103) I have listed some structural changes in the organization of spaces that help smoothing patient flows throughout the hospital structures, for example:

- A centralized OR block helps efficiency (thanks to economies of scale) and productivity (thanks to a better scheduling process);
- The presence of a Recovery Room increases productivity and eases the pressure on ICU a typical bottleneck of the entire surgical process;
- A discharge room – a space where patients are moved after the discharge – eases the relationships between ED and wards production units that typically fight for lack of beds in the central hours of the day[12];
- A centralized outpatient platform with a single waiting area helps smoothing patient flows and reduce waiting time.

Since OM means, in the end, moving patients and materials across different spaces and settings, it is clear how the actual organization of space does matter. However – as proved by some authors (Nicosia 2010 and Marsilio et al., 2017) – re-organizing space has a positive impact on other two dimensions:

---

[12] For a more detailed description of the role of the discharge room we refer the reader to Paragraph 2.1.

- *Predisposition to change*: for example Nicosia (2010) in his work argues that the creation of a new recovery room has represented, in his hospital, an opportunity for change redesigning the surgical process and introducing new rules and procedures;
- *Knowledge sharing*: a centralized and shared environment (e.g. a centralized outpatient platform or a centralized OR block) forces doctors to share the same space and encourages informal sharing of knowledge and information.

Despite the central role of physical lay-out within OM strategies, architects and engineers tend not to listen to managers who have strategic responsibility in the design and execution of healthcare production processes. It is, thus, important to set up multidisciplinary teams capable of handling logistical projects under different perspectives.

Another important driver for redesigning hospital Operations Management system is the *organization of processes and activities*. As already mentioned, it has been quite a few years that healthcare organizations redesign production processes by centralizing functions and assets with the goal of improving efficiency and productivity and taking advantage of economies of scale and standardization. This holds true for both patient flow logistics and supply chain management. In this latter case, we assist, for example, to the recent trend of centralizing the warehouse's management at regional or provincial level [13].

Another key driver in the redesign of healthcare production processes is represented by the "make" or "buy" choice. Lately, especially in the case of supply chain management, many activities such as (i) warehouse management; (ii) transportation and distribution to the wards; (iii) RFiD tagging are delegated to external providers. The Paragraph 3.4 is dedicated to illustrate pros, cons and organizational conditions of these partnerships.

When we look at patient flow logistics, the current trend is to move towards horizontal process-based organizations, with the final goal of going beyond the vertical specialty-based, which turned out to be inefficient and also less effective and patient-centred, due to a lack of coordination between the different organizational units involved along the full cycle of care. In this text, we will analyze pros, cons and organizational conditions to facilitate this innovation process presenting, in particularly, three different approaches/models, namely:

1. the patient-centered model (Paragraph 2.4);

---

[13] We refer the reader to Chapter 3.5 where we describe, in details, the case of the logistical platform ESTAV.

2. the focused hospital model (Paragraph 4.4);
3. the lean thinking approach (Paragraph 4.1).

Finally, in terms of *information and technological aspects*, the current frontier of innovation surely offers interesting opportunities to improve the performance of OM system. The most relevant need is to have real-time information about the status of each single input either patient or supply. For example, in the case of patient flows logistics, it is important, for each patient, to know where he/she is now, where he/she is planned to go next and what needs to be done to move the patient further along the care chain. A few years ago, as part of a jury of experts, we rewarded, as best lean (cfr. Infra) project, a visual management model applied to the management of a recovery room: at any given time, all healthcare professionals have an immediate understanding of the situation of each patient and a different colour signals what needs to be done to move patients to regular wards, for example "yellow" means that the anaesthesiologist check is still missing.

To control patient flow logistics, it is also important to control the status of each single production unit. For example, modern hospitals have a real-time map of the status of all hospital beds; this is particularly useful for ED people in their daily chase for a hospital bed.

Finally, in terms of technological innovation, the area of materials management has been, lately, invested by a series of important innovations likewise:

- The use of RFiD (Radio Frequency Identification) for the traceability of supplies along the whole supply chain cycle;
- Smart closets to keep medicines and medical devices at the floor;
- AGV (Automatic Guided Vehicle) for transportation;
- De-packaging systems for medicines;
- ...

Technological innovation is not such an immediate and straightforward process and it will bring the expected results in terms of quality and efficiency only if managers will be able to govern some aspects:

- the coherence of the innovation with the specificities of healthcare production processes (cfr. Paragraph 1.3);
- the level of integration and standardization of all different hospital information systems;
- the level of flexibility, that is the capability of the system to react to unexpected changes;
- the need of training for all the employees involved in the use of the new technology;

- the request of daily maintenance;
- the impact on nursing and clinical activities.

In conclusion, as summarized in Figure 7, an Operations Manager should address questions like:

1. How can I schedule my demand?
2. What is the best lay-out and organization of spaces?
3. How can I re-organize the flow of activities at my production Units?
4. What is the appropriate level of investment in technology innovation and information system?

Figure 7. The main questions of an operations manager in healthcare.

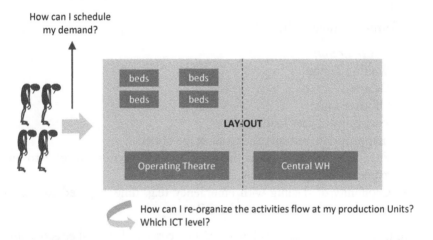

Source: author's elaboration.

1.9. Performance of Operations Management systems

Several authors have suggested different theoretical frameworks to assess the performance of OM systems. For example, according to Chase et al. (2004) the OM function should accomplish six different macro objectives: (i) quality; (ii) reliability; (iii) flexibility; (iv) speed; (v) productivity and (vi) costs reduction.

Grando et al. (2010) identify, on the contrary, other four broad performance dimensions (i) costs and productivity; (ii) quality; (iii) flexibility interpreted, in this case, as the capability of the system to deal with variety and variability of requests and (iv) timeliness in terms of speed with which new products are introduced.

In the case of healthcare, measuring OM performance is quite more complicated because there are two different main areas that respond to different logics and goals. This text will present a possible dashboard of indicators to measure patient flow logistics in Paragraph 2.1 and for supply chain management in Paragraph 3.3.

In my previous book (Villa 2012), I have divided, in particular, patient flow indicators in two broad categories:

1. *Efficiency and Productivity* with indicators like, for example:
   - Cancelled cases;
   - Utilization rates of single production units (e.g. operating rooms);
   - Average Length of Stay;
   - Throughput time (overall time necessary to get a certain process done);
   - Turn-over time at the OR.

2. *Process Indicators*
   - Waiting Times;
   - Delays;
   - OR over-time;
   - Variability of case load;
   - Inappropriate setting (due to shortage of beds);
   - Flexibility (interpreted as the capacity of the system to react to unexpected changes in demand);
   - Capability of dealing with emergency (e.g. time required to take a femur fracture patient into the OR).

In this framework, aspects like economic costs and clinical effectiveness do not entirely fall within the area of responsibility of operations managers. For example, as for the economic side, it is obvious that improving the productivity can have, with unchanged demand, an impact, at least in the long run, on costs but many critical cost drivers, like type and price of the different materials and technologies, are not under direct control of operations managers. The same reasoning holds true for clinical effectiveness: the examples provided throughout this text show that a good Operations Management system does have an impact on the final level of quality provided to patients but, at the end, clinical effectiveness depends heavily on decisions and behaviors of healthcare professionals, particularly nurses and physicians.

Paragraph 2.1 will provide extensive details about the computational algorithm to calculate patient flow logistics indicators, with a particular focus on some relevant production units such as operating room, emergency department and inpatient beds.

However, to offer, already in this chapter, some hints about possible indicators we can go back to the example of Figure 6 that represents an over-simplified flowchart of the all possible colon cancer pathway. Possible indicators to measure the overall OM performance in the management of this clinical condition are the following:

Process indicators

- Waiting time from the diagnosis to the surgical intervention;
- Waiting time from the diagnosis to the radio therapy;
- Waiting time from the diagnosis to the pharmaceutical treatment;
- Waiting time for the first specialist visit;
- Census variability at the different production units (e.g. wards);
- Cases delayed or bumped from a specific setting (e.g. oncology wards);
- ...

Efficiency indicators

- OR utilization rate;
- Average length of stay for surgical patients;
- Average length of stay at the wards before the day of the surgical intervention;
- Time necessary to complete a surgical intervention;
- ...

As we can see, we have excluded, from this dashboard, indicators of costs and clinical effectiveness. In both cases, in fact, decisions and behaviors of clinicians are decisive think, for example, to the impact of the decisions about chemotherapy agents on the overall cost or the ability of the surgeon on indicators such as mortality rate or life expectancy after intervention.

Finally, another set of consideration need to be made in the case of patients' satisfaction. Only lately, thanks to the consolidation of the theoretical framework associated to co-production and the development of measures such as PREMs (Patient Reported Experience Measures) and PROM (Patient Reported Outcome Measures), the role of patients has assumed a relevant role in the decisions about the design and execution of healthcare delivery processes. Again, the focus of OM is on other aspects, but typical OM dimensions do have an impact on patient experience. Think for example to the case of the patient Magboo described at the beginning of Paragraph 1.7: nurses and physicians were very nice at her and, at the end, the surgical intervention went very well but we cannot say that patient experience was so good since Magboo was forced to wait in front of the OR for several hours because of several operational problems.

In any case, the definition of a sound and coherent set of indicators is an essential step to set up an Operations Management function with responsibilities on the overall healthcare chain. In this respect, we need to positively evaluate the recent trend, recorded in different healthcare organizations in Italy as well as abroad, to create OM offices.

In this process it is, however, important to avoid three different types of mistake:

1. believing that the mere creation of an office labelled "Operations Management" can actually solve the many operational problems healthcare delivery organizations are currently suffering;
2. overloading this new function with high responsibilities and overlooking the importance of managing the interdependencies with the other organizational components;
3. wasting time in useless battles to decide which is the best background or best office to manage this function. In fact, different case studies (Villa, 2012) show that this new function can be successfully taken over by different divisions such as (i) medical direction; (ii) nursing direction; (iii) new offices created "ad hoc" to manage this new function or (iii) other preexisting offices with an extension of their responsibilities (e.g. the planning and control or quality office).

1.10. Reengineering public sector production: the case of Boston Housing Authority [14]

As explained in the introduction, we conclude each chapter with one or more teaching cases. The case reported at the end of this chapter is the only one not being related to healthcare and it is aimed to exemplify the impact of public sector specificities in the design and execution of OM strategies.

In particular, the case deals with the sector of public housing. Public housing refers to properties managed and rented to tenants at affordable rents. The purpose of this public service is to provide affordable housing to people and families on low incomes and it is allocated based on need.

In July 1979, Mr. Spence became the new General Director of Boston

---

[14] The case has been written on the basis of a series of interviews carried out by the author in two distinct periods: firstly in 2003 and, subsequently, in 2017. A special thanks goes to Pam Goodman, former Beacon Communities CEO and Bill McGonagle, former BHA Director. Finally, part of the information, included in the case, has been drawn from the book "Creating Public Value" edited by Moore (1997).

Housing Authority (BHA). He was appointed by the Massachusetts Department of Housing and Community Development to fix a very problematic situation. The previous management had demonstrated to be incompetent and irresponsible. Now Mr. Spence is called to "take any and all actions necessary, desirable, and appropriate" to make the BHA able to achieve its mission and meet the expectations of all main stakeholders.

The situation at the moment of Spence's appointment

The Boston Housing Authority (BHA) was the largest landlord in Boston and the largest public housing authority in New England[15]. BHA houses approximately 10 percent of the city's residents through its programs. The Authority receives federal and state assistance in order to operate these programs and, as such, is governed by any applicable housing regulations issued by the U.S. Department of Housing and Urban Development and the Massachusetts Department of Housing and Community Development.

The U.S. Department of Housing and Urban Development (HUD) provided about $20 million annually to subsidize the BHA's operations. This amount was dictated by a formula estimating how much it should cost a well-managed housing authority to operate projects of the stile, vintage, and construction of those managed by the BHA. Massachusetts State contributed another $7 million, and the BHA collected an additional $7 million from its tenants in rental income.

At the moment of Spence's appointment, BHA was facing serious and compelling problems. The authority was plagued by a $5 million debt, a vacancy rate of 28% (twice that of any other large authority), appalling maintenance, inadequate security and rampant vandalism. The vacancy rate did not reflect a lack of applicants – there were some 8,000 people on the waiting list at any given time. Rather, apartments were empty because they were simply uninhabitable.

Furthermore, rental income fell, current tenants owed $1.4 million in uncollected rents. Declining revenues forced deferred maintenance, which led to deteriorating physical conditions, and this in turn stimulated vandalism, further depressing the quality of the housing supply. The end result was too often a ghastly landscape of mutilated buildings, broken glass, empty apartments, abandoned automobiles, litter, and garbage, a wasteland hostage to the criminal, vagrant, truant and street gang; a hazard to the passerby and a nightmare to the residents.

---

[15] For New England we intend the north-east area of United States. This area includes six States: Maine, New Hampshire, Massachusetts, Vermont, Connecticut e Rhode Island.

The tenant population was increasingly impoverished, with nearly 80% of the resident families containing no wage-earning members. Tenant incomes ranged from $3,700 to $6,400 per year, the lowest of any housing authority in the nation. Furthermore, the projects were racially homogeneous and growing more so: from 13,5% minority in 1960 to 33% in 1969 to 44% by 1975. These figures, combined with the high number of minors (9% of the minor population of Boston, 20% of its adolescent population) and of elderly people (about 7% of the city's elderly inhabitants) made for an overall tenancy that contained in the words of a 1975 BHA study, "a large proportion of persons and families who are the concern of social policy in the fields of public assistance, community solidarity, police issues, racial affairs and others".

The organization at BHA

About 700 people worked for BHA. They were distributed across two major divisions:

(i)   Division of Planning, Development, and Modernization and
(ii) Division of Operations.

About 200 worked in administrative positions in the Division of Planning, Development, and Modernization. They were in charge of making plans, budgeting, purchasing, keeping accounts and personnel.

The core of the activities was carried out by the Division of Operations where 500 people worked on different activities:

(i)   rents collection;
(ii) tenant's selection;
(iii) buildings maintenance;
(iv) security;
(v)   services to tenants.

The Division of Operations divided its work by function and program. One Unit was responsible for building maintenance; another for security; a third for rents collection and tenants' selection; and a fourth for tenant services.

Among the BHA's 700 employees, many of whom owed their jobs to political connections in City Hall, both morale and productivity were low: the response time to requests for maintenance work could run as high as 69 days. At the same time, however, maintenance workers received unusually and burdensomely high pay, the result of state regulations controlling blue collar wage rates at the BHA.

In addition, the division employed 30 people as project managers. Their task was "to ensure the efficient operation and management" of one or more particular housing projects. Over the years, however, project managers had lost direct control over rent collection, tenant selection, and transfers since these functions had been centralized and, as a consequence, the power of the project managers to shape life in the individual projects drained away.

Administratively, the authority was casual; although data of various sort was complied, it did not appear to be put to use within the organization. Performance measures ranged from ineffective to non-existent, cost information was hard to come by, project managers had no input into the budgeting process, and little information was aggregated by specific projects.

Progress tended to be measured in terms of dollar spent, units of housing produced, construction wages generated, or number of units of dilapidated housing demolished rather than the amount of quality housing-in-use supplied to poor. Yet measuring the success of a public housing program in terms of employment provided, slums cleared, or even units built it is like measuring success of a medical operation in terms of amount of time taken, number of persons involved, or the surgeon's fee.

The difficult challenge for Mr. Spence

Spence was called to fix a very desperate situation and he needed to sort things out quickly. However, there were different open issues. First, which was the mission and the strategic focus of BHA. Spence started with the assumption that BHA's goal was to provide decent, publicly owned and subsidized housing to those who, by virtue of their poverty, deserved it. However, lately BHA had been receiving pressures to preserve the quality of the housing it owned and to become financially self-sufficient – goals that seemed to be, to some degree, in conflict with the initial mission of focusing its resources on the desperately poor.

Secondly, he knew, after a series of meetings with the top management, that, at BHA, processes were really bad designed and executed. Operations continued to suffer from misunderstandings, mistakes, unnecessary steps and missed deadlines and, above other things, there was no attention at all to the clients' needs and expectations.

The truth was that he did not have a clue on where to start. It seemed that everybody within the organization had his/her own priorities and it was difficult to balance everything out.

Some top managers believed that high top priority had to be assigned to the collecting process: improve collections could produce a quick-win and, if sustained, guarantee continuing higher revenues into the future that could provide financial resources to finance the investments necessary to repair the buildings, most of them old and deteriorated. This potential revenue source was limited by two important rules, however. The first required the BHA to rent only to those people whose incomes were less than 80% of the area's median income. The second prohibited the BHA from charging tenants more than 25% on their annual income in rents.

To citizens and overseers who thought the agency contributed the most value by being a good and generous landlord to Boston's poorest residents, these rules were fundamental to ensuring that it achieved its purpose. To citizens and managers who sought to ensure the BHA's continued financial viability, however, and who were willing to sacrifice some of the benefits to the poorest for achieving this somewhat different purpose, the rules were an unfortunate obstacle. Indeed, they were forcing the BHA down a path toward ruin.

Another problem was the level of security. There was evidence in the high turnover rate that fear of crime was driving tenants out, or at least those who could find housing elsewhere. Police coverage was notoriously inadequate – and residents of public housing claimed that police would not venture at all into the more troubled developments, especially those largely inhabited by minorities.

Some others sustained that the very first thing to do was to computerize the processes: everything was handled on paper copy, the level of Information Technology was generally low. Some managers from the Division of Operations made the argument that significant investments in this direction had to be considered a "must" for the organization: an injection of new technologies and Information Systems was a necessary first step to start an extensive program of business processes re-engineering.

Spence personally believed that one of the priority was the tenants selection process and so instructed one of his collaborators to "dig deep" into this process to find out the weaknesses and recommend possible solutions.

Tenant selection was, at least, in theory a two-step process. First, families had to be eligible to apply for public housing; the only important criterion at this stage was meeting whatever was the current federal definition of low-income household. Once income eligibility was established – by requiring the applicants to produce documentation from their employers, the Department of Welfare, Social Security or whatever – the authority had next to grapple with the delicate issue of tenant screening and of deciding who on the waiting list (which never had fewer than several thousands of applicants on it) would get into the 1,800 or so units that became available each year.

Under the BHA's old policies, any application for BHA residency triggered a complete investigation of the applicant's eligibility and suitability, which was then updated annually. That process would have made sense if immediate prospects for occupancy existed. But the waiting list held eight thousand names! The average time spent waiting for residence was several years. Many applicants moved (or even died) before being admitted. Something was wrong, according to Spence, the tenant selection process was in need of major re-construction. It needed to be managed more quickly and in a more flexible manner.

For example, Spence found out that BHA had serious difficulties in getting refrigerators to a vacant unit. The apartment could remain empty for a long time until a refrigerator was found. It was necessary to manage the waiting list more flexibly. So, in the words of Spence, *"...we can start from the family that's number one on the waiting list, we have a unit for you. If you can work and provide your own refrigerator, we can move you in immediately"*. *"And the family – a mother of three children- would say, "I don't see how I can do that, I can't afford a refrigerator"*. And the BHA would say *"Well, then, as soon as we can get a refrigerator, we'll admit you. You're not losing your place on the waiting list."* But they'll go to number two and ask, *"Can you move in and fix this place up?"* And if the second household on the waiting list has a male head of the household, and they are both working, and they can afford a refrigerator, the BHA will move them in first.

However, some managers within the same staff of Mr. Spence, were questioning this change in the tenant selection process:

"Let's suppose you have somebody who's been on a waiting list for five years, but they're on welfare, and you'd much rather admit somebody who applied yesterday who has a job" "Is it fair to do that?" "We need to define explicit and clear eligibility criteria and stick to that otherwise we would create room for misbehaviors and favoritisms. We definitely cannot tolerate that".

Spence was also aware that something was wrong in the all process that it took to actually get a new refrigerator. The process started from the project managers that were in charge of checking the state of the art of the vacant apartments. Unfortunately, since project managers did not have any staff to support them, a refrigerator could remain broken with nobody knowing about it for months. Once realized that an apartment had a refrigerator broken, the project manager needed to place an order to the Division of Operations (Unit in charge of building maintenance), the Unit was in charge to sort out all the requests coming from the different projects, check if the refrigerator needed to be replaced and, if so, place an order to the BHA warehouse. The BHA warehouse checked the in-house availability of refrigerators. In case no refrigerator was available, the building maintenance Unit needed to place an order proposal to the people working at the Division of Planning, Development, and Modernization. Quite a long process especially if you think that everything was run, at that time, on paper.

Finally, Spence was not sure if the current heavy centralization was, in effect, a good idea. The previous BHA management judged that efficiencies could be gained by centralizing common, functions across projects. Every housing project did not need its own plumber, furnace repairer, or tenant screener; these job could be performed by centralized personnel deployed where needed. In addition centralizing these functions would enhance consistency. One project would not receive advantages over another because it had a manager who was particularly determined about maintenance, for example. But most importantly, a centralized structure allows a much more uniform and equitable access. The eligibility criteria are clear and go to the advantage of the poorest component of the community. With a more decentralized structure there is the risk to make the tenants selection process less transparent and equitable.

This was true, but, on the contrary, the centralized units did not understand any particular project but were specialized in knowing how to perform a particular function across all the projects. As a consequence, as the power of the project managers was reduced, the organization lost its sense of responsibility for the overall product. Implicitly, midlevel managers and employees felt more responsible for satisfying central managers than for responding to clients who lived in the projects. In fact, almost nothing in the BHA's administrative systems focused the staff on the accomplishment of its mission. BHA's clients had to reach the center of the organization to get a response, although they could not be sure the center would provide one. Finally, as a direct consequence of this type of organizational structure, the information available at level of single project was only the data about the tenants who failed to pay the rent. All other information about costs, activities, and performance were aggregated for the organization as a whole, or for particular functions such as maintenance or security.

Furthermore, in this scenario project managers were left without authority or means to handle basic functions such as maintenance, rent collection, tenant selection and eviction. These managers were, by and large, of indifferent ability; some were characterized as being totally inadequate. Yet they bore the brunt of tenants complaints and concerns.

After all, Spence was considering the idea to reverse the BHA's tendency to centralize functions. Specifically, Spence believed that some functions

– like maintenance and security – were better performed if decentralized at the level of each single project. Furthermore, Spence wanted to increase the responsibility for local project managers. A better situation would be a situation where project managers, instead of receiving money and personnel according to the dictates of the central office, determined their own priorities.

Furthermore, another idea of Spence was that a way to overcome part of the BHA's problems was to empower the same BHA clients. They should be encouraged to (i) take care of the buildings, (ii) testify against incorrect behaviors carried out by other tenants; (iii) promote the quality of life at BHA's properties and so on. To this regard Spence was evaluating the opportunity to organize, under the umbrella of BHA's activities, alternative programs such as job-training, informational sessions, social initiatives and so. He was not sure though if include this type of activities under BHA direct responsibility or alternatively ask the help for other non-profit organization in the Boston area more well equipped and experienced in organizing this type of activities.

The time available to fix all these problems was short and the situation was extremely complicated. Spence had to deal with an extremely wide range of issues, managerial and political, under intense pressure from tenants (a group of whom had already started a class action suit) and scrutiny and involvement from the public, the federal government, the State and the city of Boston.

Spence was aware of the difficult situation and anxious to resolve all the problems, but felt that he did not understand the details of the all BHA activities. He felt he needed a much more thorough understanding of the flow and characteristics of BHA's processes.

Chapter 2
PATIENT FLOW LOGISTICS

SUMMARY: 2.1. Model of analysis and indicators. – 2.2. Operating Room Performance Indicators. – 2.3. Optimizing patient flows at Emergency Department (ED). – 2.4. The patient-centred hospital model. – 2.5. Improving Quality through redesign of hospital patient flow logistics: the case of Boston Medical Centre. – 2.6. Sasso hospital. – Reorganizing hospital wards around intensity of care: how & why?

2.1. Model of analysis and indicators

As outlined in chapter one, managing operations in the healthcare sector means optimizing two different types of flow: (i) patient flows and (ii) materials. This chapter is entirely dedicated to patient flow logistics. Particularly, the first paragraph presents a general theoretical framework to assess hospital patient flows' performance while the following focus on specific production units: operating room (Paragraph 2.2); emergency department (Paragraph 2.3) and wards (Paragraph 2.4).

Together with the colleagues Prenestini and Giusepi (Villa et al., 2014), through a comparative study of six Italian hospitals, I have built a framework to analyse the performance of hospital patient flow systems.

The framework adopts a system-wide approach to patient flow management and is structured around three different levels:

(1) the hospital;
(2) the pipelines (possible patient journeys within the hospital);
(3) the production units (physical spaces, such as operating rooms, where service delivery takes places).

This theoretical model has been conceived around the idea that a hospital is a complex system made of several internal sub-components that are interdependent from each other. In order to implement successful OM strategies it is critical to address the overall cycle of care, from the very first access to the discharge and follow-up. Partial approaches that focus only on single hospital resources or on discrete interventions, rather than the full production cycle, tend to lead the overall system to suboptimal results. Consequently, meaningful and effective patient flow strategies need to adopt a system-wide approach.

Several authors have suggested different theories and models to explain the actual source of hospital patient flow problems.

One relevant aspect outlined by different authors (De Vries at al., 1999; Walley and Steyn, 2006; Litvak E., Bisognano M., 2011; Villa et al., 2014) is that patient flow problems occur when hospital resources (such as beds, operating rooms and nursing staff) are allocated in a fixed way and not updated on a regular basis, reflecting the distribution of the historical rights of the practitioners rather than the actual patient-related demands.

Vissers identifies three different factors that cause patient flow problems (Vissers, 1998; Vissers and De Vries):

(i)   capacity shortage: the amount of a resource available to a production unit may not be in balance with the demand for that resource at the average level of production;

(ii) patient flow variability: the timing of the allocation of resources to a unit may lead to peaks and troughs; for example, if operating room sessions are not well allocated during the week, large variations in the demand for beds and nursing staff may result;

(iii) lack of coordination: the capacities of the various resources that are required simultaneously by different specialties may not be balanced, resulting in bottlenecks or under-utilization.

In the study conducted with Prenestini and Giusepi (Villa et al., 2014) we have identified six different possible main causes of patient flow problems:

(i)   bad allocation of capacity;

(ii) shortage of capacity;

(iii) variability;

(iv) lack of coordination between the different hospital production units (e.g. operating room, ICU or regular floors);

(v)   presence of bottlenecks [1] along the whole hospital chain that delay the patient throughput;

(vi) overlapping between elective and emergency/urgency cases.

In order to realize a comprehensive appraisal of hospital patient flow performance, we have tried to incorporate all these dimensions in our theoretical model. Specifically, we developed an analytical framework organized around three different levels (see Figure 1) where each level of the model focuses on one or more of these dimensions.

---

[1] The bottleneck is the limiting factor stopping the patient flows from going smoothly through the healthcare pathway.

Figure 1. Theoretical framework to measure patient flow logistics.

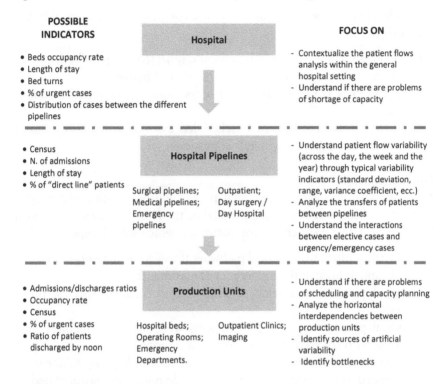

Source: adapted from Villa (2012).

As shown in the figure, the framework unfolds around three different levels:

1. *Hospital*
   In this case, the main goals are to contextualize the patient flow analysis within the general hospital context and to determine whether there are situations of capacity shortage that create patient flow problems.

2. *Hospital pipelines*
   In this phase of the analysis, the goal is to understand (i) patient flow variability (across the day, the week and the year) and (ii) the interactions between the different pipelines.

3. *Production units*
   In this case, the analysis narrows down to level of each single production unit with the aim of understanding whether there are specific problems of capacity or scheduling and identify bottlenecks and possible sources of artificial variability.

Hospital

At this level of analysis, it is possible to use common and traditional indicators such as:

Bed Utilization Rate = (yearly treatment days)/(365*hospital beds);
Bed Turns= (Total Inpatient Cases)/(number of beds);
Length of Stay (LOS) = (treatment days)/(number of inpatient admissions);
% of urgent cases = (urgent unscheduled cases admitted to the hospital[2])/(overall number of hospitals admissions).

Hospital pipelines

If we consider the various potential patient journeys within the hospital (from the patient's arrival at the hospital to the final discharge), it is possible to identify five distinct physical pathways (which we call pipelines):

1. emergency pipelines (physical pathways travelled by patients who access the hospital through the Emergency Department);
2. surgical pipelines (referring to patients undergoing a surgical procedure);
3. medical pipelines (referring to patients who only need medical treatment and do not pass through the operating room);
4. day-surgery/day-hospital (referring to patients undergoing minor surgical procedures or medical treatments and do not need a hospital bed);
5. outpatient (referring to patients who stay, within the hospital, for a few hours during a medical or diagnostic visit).

The identification of these five mutually exclusive pipelines was made crossing three different dimensions:

(i) the type of production units used (e.g., medical wards vs. surgical wards);
(ii) the type of demand met (particularly scheduled vs. unscheduled cases) and
(iii) the patient's length of stay within the hospital (e.g., patients in the outpatient pipeline who use hospital infrastructures just for a few hours).

It is important to stress how each pipeline passes through different possible production units (the third level of this analysis) that can be exclusively assigned to a single specific pipeline (e.g., operating room or surgical

---

[2] In this case, we are not referring to actual clinical urgencies but to all those unscheduled cases that are admitted to the hospital without any previous notice.

beds in the case of surgical pipeline) or can be shared between different pipelines; for example, a CT-scan can be used, alternatively, by different hospital pipelines.

Finally, it is, however, important not to confuse the production pipelines described in this paragraph with the clinical pathways (see Par. 1.5). The clinical pathways consist of the series of physician and nursing activities performed with sub-groups of patients who are homogeneous under a clinical perspective, but not under a logistics perspective. In fact, clinical pathways related to complex conditions may cross different hospital production pipelines. For example, a colon cancer patient who has been diagnosed during an outpatient visit (outpatient pipeline) will perform the preoperative screening in the Outpatient Department (outpatient pipeline) before undergoing surgery (ordinary surgical pipeline). Finally, after surgery, he/she might be required to go through pharmaceutical treatment in a day hospital (day hospital pipeline).

Production Units
The final stage of the analysis focuses on the single production units that, in the case of a hospital, are represented by:

(i)   operating rooms;
(ii)   emergency department;
(iii) wards;
(iv)   diagnostics;
(v)   outpatient platforms.

The theoretical framework depicted in Figure 1 considers all the different dimensions of patient flow logistics identified in the scientific literature. For example, the issue of capacity shortage is captured at the hospital level, the analysis of patient flow variability is examined at pipeline level while problems of scheduling or bottlenecks are caught at the level of single production unit.

At hospital level, a simple but quite effective graphic representation is given by the two-by-two matrix that crosses two different dimensions: (i) bed-utilization rate and (ii) bed turns (see Figure 2).

Figure 2. Two-by-Two Matrix Bed Turns vs. Beds Utilization Rate.

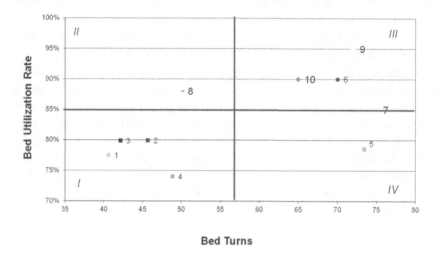

Bed Turns

Source: adapted from Villa (2012).

Hospitals in quadrant III (high utilization rates and high bed turns) have been really running at their maximum capacity and, therefore, they can rightfully claim that patient flow problems are due to shortage of resources and that it is necessary to invest in extra capacity, in this case, more beds. A recent study conducted by Friebel and coullegues (Friebel et al., 2019) shows a correlation between beds' occupancy and the 30 days readmissions rate particularly in the older and sicker patient population, indicating possible problems in the discharge process under the pressure of freeing space for new incoming patients in situations of stress for lack of enough capacity.

On the contrary, in the case of quadrant I, patient flow problems, such as delays, long waiting, are not due to capacity shortage but to faulty decisions about the design and execution of hospital OM system.

For more than fifteen years, I have been the coordinator of the so called **LLP (Laboratorio Logistica del Paziente)** a patient flows community managed jointly by two different research centers: (i) CERISMAS (Research Center on Healthcare Management), Università Cattolica del Sacro Cuore and (ii) CRC HEAD, Research Center of Health Administration, Università degli Studi di Milano. It is a community of hospitals interested in carrying out benchmarking analysis on patient flow logistics' performance. Evidence collected across all these years show that, in most of the cases, patient flow issues are not related to shortage of capacity but, rather, to uncontrolled artificial variability or lack of coordination between different production units.

At pipeline level, as indicated in Chapter 1, a key aspect is the control of variability of patient arrivals. This variability determines peaks and valleys in the demand for hospital resources and creates queues, delays and stress for the hospital personnel. Therefore, it is important to identify and eliminate artificial variability.

Figure 3. Census[3] Variability at surgical pipeline.

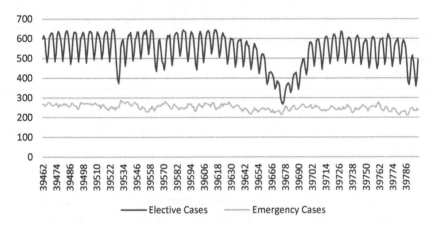

Source: authors' elaborations from LLP data.

The pattern shown in this Figure is very similar to the trends recorded in the other hospitals belonging to our patient flows community network. This circumstance outlines two important aspects. First, despite common beliefs, the urgent/unscheduled cases are less variable at aggregate level and much more predictable than the elective cases. As confirmed by other studies (Litvak et al., 2005; Villa, 2012), the presumably controllable flow of patients who are scheduled to arrive for elective procedures is, in fact, more variable from day to day and week to week than the flow of patients being admitted due to emergencies, who are, on the contrary, more predictable and stable over time. Secondly, we can solve the problem of unscheduled emergency/urgent cases by setting aside a certain amount of capacity that is pretty stable over time, in the case above roughly 350 beds.

---

[3] Census represents the daily number of patients present at ward.

If the final goal is to address the actual sources of artificial variability, then it is necessary to extend the analysis to each production unit. In the case of the surgical pipeline, a critical production unit that deeply influences the throughput time for the whole chain is represented by the operating room.

For this reason, the next Paragraph (2.2) is entirely dedicated to the analysis of ORs' performance.

Finally, our theoretical model represents also a useful tool to assess the coordination between the different pipelines and production unit within a hospital that is often a cause of patient flow problems.

The study conducted with the colleagues Prenestini and Giusepi (Villa et al., 2014) shows that the daily distribution of admissions and discharges has an impact on the ED length of stay (the amount of time from the moment the patient arrives to the moment the patient leaves).

In particular, the study shows a negative correlation between the discharges/admissions ratio and the ED length of stay; that is, as the inpatient discharges/admissions ratio increases, the following day ED length of stay consequently decreases.

This result is confirmed by other studies (Foster et al., 2003; Vermeulen et al., 2009; Litvak and Bisognano, 2011) which show how, when beds on the floors are full, patients who come in through the emergency department cannot be admitted in a timely manner. Consequently, backups occur and patients are boarded in the hallways.

As it will be further illustrated in the Paragraph dedicated to the ED (Paragraph 2.3) these problems are due to a mismatch between the time ED patients are admitted and the time hospitalized patients are discharged. The ED is a production unit that fills up in the morning; roughly, 15-20% of these patients are kept in the hospital, so they require a bed. In contrast, wards discharge the majority of their patients after noon, thus creating a mismatch between supply and demand and this, in turn, causes daily fights for inpatient beds during the central hours of the day (see Figure 4).

Figure 4. Daily disequilibrium between ED arrivals and hospital discharges.

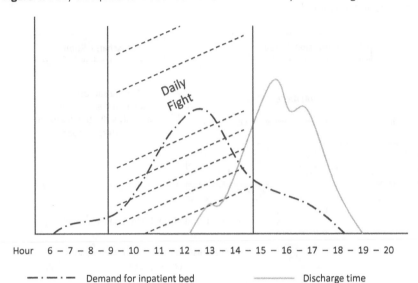

Hour   6 – 7 – 8 – 9 – 10 – 11 – 12 – 13 – 14 – 15 – 16 – 17 – 18 – 19 – 20

— · — · — Demand for inpatient bed   ——————— Discharge time

Source: authors' elaboration.

As illustrated in Figure 5, a possible downstream solution is to create an area buffer called Discharge Room where to accommodate patients after the discharge waiting for somebody to bring then back home. In this case, it is possible to free up a bed to assign to patients coming from the ED. Of course, this solution works only if hospital is equipped to discharge patients by noon, alternatively the Discharge Room will remain empty without any type of effect on ED waiting time and overcrowding[4].

An alternative "upstream" solution is to create the so-called admissions' area, located inside the ED dedicated to those patients waiting for a bed at the hospital. During this temporary stay it is possible to start the diagnostics and treatment pathway. This type of solution is more costly, if compared to the Discharge Room scenario, since it requires doctors and technology. However, this unit can be used to accommodate patients who arrive at the ED during the night thus avoiding, in this sense, nightly admissions that usually create confusion at the floor.

---

[4] The study conducted by Pagliantini and colleagues (Pagliantini et al., 2009) describes in details the successful implementation of the Discharge Room at Siena Teaching Hospital.

Figure 5. Possible logistical solutions to deal with the hourly mismatch between ED arrivals and inpatient beds' availability.

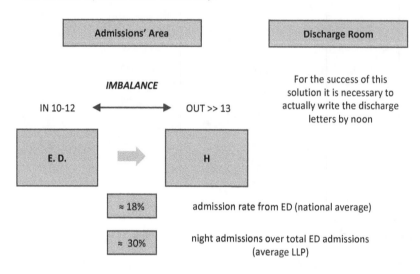

Source: authors' elaboration.

In conclusion, we can reasonably say that the theoretical model illustrated in this book can be considered an appropriate tool to assess the hospital patient flow performance for, at least, two different sets of considerations. First, as already mentioned, it is critical to adopt a system-wide approach to patient flow management and, therefore, contextualize any specific analysis within the overall hospital context (the first level of our analysis). Secondly, the different possible elements (as those found in the scientific literature and those that arose during the focus groups regularly organized within our patient flow community network LLP) explaining hospital patient flow problems are to be found at different levels and are often due to a lack of coordination between pipeline and production units.

The model presented in this paragraph represents a useful framework to build a system-wide dashboard to monitor hospital patient flow logistics' performance. It is, however, important to alert the reader about some possible warnings.

First of all, it is necessary to check the validity and reliability of each indicator. Reliability has to with the degree to which the measure is free from random error (chance variation). It is, thus, important to check if the collection and computational process are free of error. Validity is the degree to which the measure is associated with the construct aims to measure. Especially in the healthcare, sometimes, we use faulty metrics that guide managers and policy makers towards misleading decisions. For example, it is valid to measure the quality of a highly specialized surgical specialty (e.g. cardiac surgery or neuro surgery) only on the basis on non-adjusted mortality rates, or it is valid measuring the operational performance of an ICU only based on utilization rate?

Secondly, the construction of a reliable and thorough OM controlling dashboard clashes sometimes with some drawbacks of the typical structure of the hospital information systems. In this sense, we can identify, at least, four different sources of problems.

First, the databases built for each production unit typically use different patient identification codes; thus, it is very difficult to keep track of the entire patient journey, especially if he/she crosses various pipelines and production units. It is, thus, important to identify a unique and anonymous patient identification number in compliance with the most recent laws about privacy.

Second, there are often different interpretations of the same data – even within the same hospital – resulting in serious problems with data reliability.

Third, some data (for example, the ED length of stay or the number of OR accesses) present serious problems of reliability.[5]

Fourthly, some data, useful for setting up effective patient flow control systems are, in most of the cases analyzed, not collected, such as: (i) the hourly stays of patients in ICUs, (ii) the exact hour of patient discharge, and (iii) the internal transfers between hospital pipelines and production units.

These considerations also help sketching some useful insights for policy makers (regional governments, states or the European Union).

First, to support the development of better patient flow management systems at the hospital level, institutions should require from hospitals (public and accredited by the national health care service) homogeneous and standardized indicators of patient flow logistics. The framework presented in this text represents a useful starting point. The definition of a minimum set of indicators is a necessary prerequisite for the definition of the basic characteristics of the hospital information systems necessary to effectively support patient flow management programs. The development of a common methodological framework to support analysis and changes in patient flow management is also a prerequisite to carry out meaningful benchmarking initiatives both at national and international level. Further-

---

[5] For example, in the case of ED, the exit triage coding is missing or wrongly recorded. The times for entry and exit of the patient from the OR are not always accurate making the indicators about OR utilization not very reliable.

more, the results of these benchmarking analyzes should favor the diffusion of standards and best practices thus contributing, in such a way, to strengthen a regional, national or even European identity of hospital care.

2.2. Operating Room Performance Indicators

In the case of operating rooms, OM should be designed to achieve two different relevant goals:

1. Reducing the overall throughput time [6] to increase productivity and
2. Optimizing the actual use of the OR through a better scheduling system capable to avoid voids, peaks and valleys.

If we stick to the first goal, the patient pathway, within the OR block, is characterized by many steps. If we take the mere operations' perspective, the final goal is to reduce the overall throughput time represented by the time required to complete the entire surgical process (including the set-up time) and being ready to treat the next patient. Reducing this time, in fact, means speeding up the entire surgical process with a consequently improvement of the overall efficiency and productivity of the system.

As represented in Table 1 the surgical process within the OR block consists of five main times [7]:

1. Waiting time of the patient before entering the OR;
2. Anaesthesia time;
3. Surgical time (First Incision – Last Suture);
4. Waking procedures of the patient;
5. Set-Up time that consists of all the necessary cleaning activities to make the room available for the next patient.

As illustrated in Table 1 these times are profoundly different.

Waiting time and set-up time can be reduced through a different organizational model of activities while waking time and anesthesia time are "clinical" time and cannot be reduced through managerial interventions.

However, in this latter case, if the operational goal is to reduce the overall throughput time within the OR it is possible to perform these activities outside with a different layout of the OR block. Particularly, the anesthesia activities can be performed in the so-called induction area while it is

---

[6] In general, the throughput time is considered as the time necessary for a unit of output to pass through a production unit.

[7] In reality, there is a time that we do not consider: the nursing time dedicated to the preparation of the patient for the intervention.

possible to wake up the patient outside the OR in the so-called recovery room. This area, besides a better use of the operating theatre[8] time, allows also to ease the pressure on ICU; in fact, this holding area consents an observational time before making the decision about the following destination of the patient: either critical care or regular wards.

Table 1. The main times of patient flow within the OR block.

Throughput Time →

	WAITING	ANESTHESIA	SURGERY	WAKING	SET-UP
Can I reduce this time?	YES	NO	NO	NO	YES
How?	Different **organization of production processes**: • Reduction in the delay of the first surgical procedure • Better coordination with the floors • Optimization of transportations • Lean methodologies				
Can we do it out of the OR?	NO	YES	NO	YES	NO
How?	Different **lay-out and organization of space** • Room for anesthesia • Recovery Room				

Source: authors' elaboration.

As already explained (cfr. Paragraph 1.8), OR scheduling is another important driver to improve the overall patient flows logistics performance. We have, in this case, three different levels of control:

1. Strategic
   Strategic decisions about the volume and case-mix of the surgical production of the next year.
2. Tactical
   Once the strategic scenario is set, it is necessary to allocate the weekly time slots to the different specialties. This process is a reminiscent of the school timetable where each hour is assigned to a class (e.g. math or history), in this case each time slot is associated to a specialty like for example Monday morning to general surgery, Monday afternoon to vascular surgery, Tuesday all day to orthopedics and so on.

---

[8] Operating Room is sometimes called operating theatre because, in the past, surgeries were actually performed in the theatres in order to permit medical students to learn from senior surgeons.

3. Operational

Finally, every week (ideally on Friday for the following week) each specialty is required to come up with the list of the names of the patients that need to undergo surgery. There is also a day-to-day scheduling activity due to natural variability elements (e.g. fever of the patient) or artificial variability (e.g. lack of the equipment).

In order to evaluate the overall OM performance of an Operating Room we present, in this text, a dashboard of indicators summarized in Table 2.

Table 2. Possible dashboard of indicators to measure OR performance.

Logistical driver	Indicator	Computational algorithm	Meaning
Capacity planning (to avoid voids and variability)	OR utilization rate	$\sum$ (time patient gets IN the OR − time patient gets OUT the OR) / (Overall OR time availability)	Analysis of the actual usage of the OR
	Over time	(time of OR utilization beyond the regular scheduled time) / (scheduled time)	Evaluation of the capability of staying in the scheduled time.
	% of elective surgical cases bumped	(number of elective surgical cases postponed) / (total number of surgical cases planned)	Capability of the scheduling system to assure an equilibrated workload distribution
	Timeliness of surgical intervention for emergency cases	Time of surgical intervention − time patient's arrival to the hospital E.D.	Capability of the hospital in dealing with surgical emergency cases
Lay-out and organization of processes (to speed-up the throughput time)	Delay of the first arrival	Time difference between first patient in the OR and scheduled opening time.	It measures the level of coordination with the wards and the level of optimization of the transportation's system. It is also a possible indicator of the presence of misbehaviors from surgeons or anesthetists.
	Turn-Over Time	Time differences between the exit of the patient from an OR and the entry of the following patient.	A measurement of the effectiveness of the cleaning procedures
	% of surgical time	Percentage of surgical time out of the total time spent by the patient in the OR	With high values of this percentage you are able to reduce throughput time and increasing, in this way, the overall OR productivity.

Source: authors' elaboration.

One of the main and well-known indicators is the OR utilization rate. This indicator can be calculated either at room level (the utilization rate of Room number 1) or at the level of specialty. The Figure below illustrates the master plan and the utilization rate for three different surgical specialties. A second indicator is the over time a measure to evaluate the capability of the hospital in staying within the scheduled time; even in this case the indicator can be calculated at the level of operating room or at the level of specialty.

Table 3. Master Plan and utilization rate for specialty.

Mon.	Tue.	Wed.	Thu.	Fri.
02/02/2015	03/02/2015	04/02/2015	05/02/2015	06/02/2015
09/02/2015	10/02/2015	11/02/2015	12/02/2015	13/02/2015
16/02/2015	17/02/2015	18/02/2015	19/02/2015	20/02/2015
23/02/2015	24/02/2015	25/02/2015	26/02/2015	27/02/2015

Specialty		UR		
	Bariatric Surgery	88%		
	General Surgery	71%		
	Orthopedics	83%		

Source: authors' elaboration of LLP (Laboratorio Logistica del Paziente) data.

Another important indicator to measure OR Operations Management is the percentage of surgical elective cases postponed. Few hospitals collect this type of information and even fewer analyze the reasons of these cancellations.

The Table presents some data about the number of elective surgical cases cancelled in a hospital. It is interesting, however, to notice that, on average, more than half of the cases' cancellations are due to problems in OR scheduling, an issue of artificial variability that has nothing to do with clinical reasons (e.g. patient's fever) that represent, on the contrary, elements of natural variability.

Table 4. Elective surgical cases cancelled.

Operating Room #	Interventions	Cases Bumped (a.v.)	Cases Bumped (%)	Reason of cancellation			
				Extension of the previous surgeries	Clinical Reasons	Decision of the physician	Unknown
1	112	19	17%	89%	11%	0%	0%
2	78	7	9%	57%	0%	43%	0%
3	93	8	9%	0%	50%	13%	37%
4	47	3	6%	100%	0%	0%	0%
5	46	2	4%	0%	100%	0%	0%
6	66	2	3%	0%	100%	0%	0%
7	80	1	1%	0%	0%	100%	0%
TOT.	522	42	8%	57%	24%	12%	7%

Source: authors' elaboration of LLP (Laboratorio Logistica del Paziente) data.

A final last metric to measure the overall efficacy of the OR scheduling system is the capability of the hospital in dealing with surgical emergency cases. A well-known indicator is, for example, the time to operating room of femur fracture patients; in fact, clinical evidence suggests that if the system is capable of operating these patients within 48 hours from their arrival to the hospital, the clinical recovery would be more effective and faster.

So far, we have focused on metrics to measure the capability of the OR scheduling system to achieve a balanced distribution of workloads eliminating (artificial) variability.

Table 2 includes also other types of indicators aiming to measure the speed of the entire process, likewise:

– *Delay of the first arrival*
  It measures the level of coordination with the wards and the level of optimization of the transportation system. It is also a possible indicator of the presence of misbehaviors of surgeons or anesthetists that systematically show up late on the OR block.
– *Turn-over time*
  The average of the time gap between the exit of the patient from an OR and the entry of the following patient. It is valid measure of the effectiveness of the cleaning procedures.
– *% of surgical time*
  This traditional and widely used indicator measures what is the percentage of surgical time out of the total time spent by the patient in the OR. Ideally you want to have this percentage as highest possible so you are able to reduce the throughput time increasing, thereafter, the overall OR productivity. As indicated in Table 1, to increase the surgical time it

is possible to work on the OR lay-out with the creation of an induction room for the anesthesia procedures and a recovery room for the awaking process of patients. It is important, however, to stress that for an appropriate OR scheduling it is important to consider all the five different times indicated in table 1.

Two common indicators to measure OR performance are (i) utilization rate and (ii) surgical time; it is, thus, interesting, crossing these two indicators in a two-by-two table.

As summarized in the Table 5 these two indicators have different meanings:

– A low utilization rate is a sign of a bad OR scheduling;
– A low surgical time means that there is room to speed-up some processes or to move outside the OR some activities such as patient's induction or awaking after surgery.

Ideally, a situation should be reached where both utilization rate and surgical time are high; the table below suggests possible change management solutions when this situation does not occur.

Table 5. Utilization rate vs. surgical time: possible change management solutions.

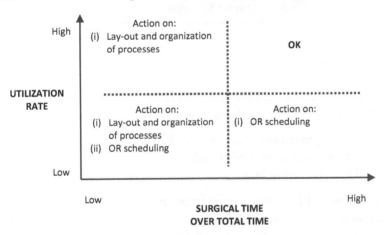

Source: authors' elaboration.

2.3. Optimizing patient flows at Emergency Department (ED)

Within the overall healthcare Operations Management system, the ED plays a relevant role since it is, together with the outpatient department, one of the two entry points to the hospital production system.

As depicted in the figure below, ED processes can be classified in four main categories:

(i)   Admission and wait for the medical visit.
(ii) Diagnostic and treatment time.
(iii) Transfer to Observation Unit.
(iv) Boarding time (wait to be admitted to the hospital).

Figure 6. ED processes

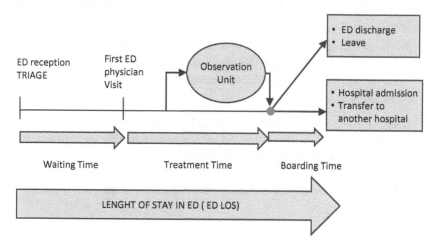

Source: authors' elaboration.

Literature review (Affleck et al., 2013) suggests three main indicators to measure ED operational performance, namely:

i.   Time to physician initial assessment (PIA);
ii. Time to transfer to in-patient bed;
iii. ED LOS (Length of Stay).

The time to PIA is the interval from arrival until the patient is seen. Patients, in general, think of this as their 'waiting time' and it is strongly correlated with patients leaving without being seen, overall patient satisfaction and ED LOS. The Canadian Association of Emergency Physicians (CAEP) recommends hospitals not to exceed 1 hour at the median and 3 hours at the 90th percentile.

Time to inpatient bed is the interval between the decision taken to hospitalize a patient and the moment he arrives in the ward. It displays the bed availability, hospital administrative efficiencies in bed management and organizing transmission of care.

Often admitted patients must wait for long times in the ED before being moved to the ward. This increases their LOS in the ED which is correlated with overall hospital LOS and mortality.

The overall ED Length of Stay (LOS) is the time span between arrival and discharge or transfer to the ward, and it displays the total experience of the patient. In Europe (e.g. UK and Italy) the standard is set to four hours. In scientific literature, this indicator is typically considered the key indicator to measure patient flows' performance of ED.

As proved by different authors (Asplin et al., 2003; Bucci et al., 2016; Marsilio et al., 2020) ED often suffers from different problems such as:

– Overcrowding.
– Excessive waiting time.
– Bad working climate and frustration among ED staff (both nurses and medical doctors).

Even the case-based evidence drawn from the recent pandemic[9] shows that the ED has been playing a central role in the management of COVID-19 patients: well-prepared and well-functioning EDs have shown better results in terms of timelines, responsiveness and capability of separate the different flows.

In scientific literature there is large consensus on the fact that the ED problems are not (only) ED problems but it is necessary to adopt a more system-wide approach. Asplin and colleagues (2003) analyze patient flows at ED using the model **input-throughput-output** sustaining the importance of looking at not only to the internal ED processes but also to the input and output components.

The input component of ED crowding includes any condition, event, or system characteristic that contributes to the demand for ED services; while the **output dimension** has to do with the interdependencies between the ED and all other down-stream facilities such as (i) inpatingt beds; (ii) other healthcare facilities; (iii) ambulatory care or (iv) home.

In the current paragraph we use this framework to classify all the possible elements, identified in the scientific literature, as possible sources of ED waiting and overcrowding.

---

[9] Quah, L.J.J., Tan, B.K.K., Fua, TP. et al. (2020) Reorganizing the emergency department to manage the COVID-19 outbreak. Int J Emerg Med 13, 32.

Input component

As for the input, different studies have focused on age as possible explicatory variable of ED overcrowding.

Leeds et al. (2006) found a disproportionate increase of elderly people (aged more than 70 years) visiting EDs in the UK. His findings are comparable with those of George et al. in 2004. They examined patient age as a possible cause of declining performance in 2004 compared with 1990. They found that elderly people had a fivefold higher rate of admission than patients aged less than 30 years. Elderly patients require more critical care, examinations and admissions. Many patients who live in residential homes suffer from severe comorbidities and are being sent to the ED for care (George et al., 2006).

With the colleagues from the center CERISMAS (Research Center on Healthcare Management), I am currently carrying out, with the hospitals associated to our research Center, a benchmarking analysis on the management of elderly at ED. The preliminary results show that elderly (over 65, over 75 and over 85) behave completely differently compared to other age clusters under different dimensions like (i) overall hospital ED LOS; (ii) gravity of the problem and (iii) hospital admissions' rate.

The management of non-emergency cases (the so-called minor codes) is a typical issue in the ED capacity planning [10].

In fact, despite the fact that, in theory, the role of the ED is to provide care for patients with sudden deterioration, or sudden and potentially severe manifestations of an acute illness or injury, in reality we observe a bigger variety of patients seeking care in the ED (Wang et al., 2018). Due to their convenience, round-the-clock care delivery, and open access (without an appointment), EDs is an attractive source of care (Cunningham et al. 2006). In this perspective, a study (Kossovsky et al., 2002) has shown how the use of a telephone hotline for outpatient providers to directly contact inpatient medical staff with the purpose of discussing of hospitalization needs decreased inappropriate admissions.

Finally, in the analysis of input's components, it is important to consider that EDs have an important "safety net" role for the vulnerable population in

---

[10] Patients presenting at an ED are classified on a categorical measurement scale aims to measure the acuity of the clinical problem. In Italy, a four-level triage system displayed with the colors red, yellow, green and white, is being used. Patients who get assigned code red fall in the highest category which means they have a life-threatening condition that needs immediate care. Code yellow represents potentially life-threatening conditions. Green portrays minor injuries or illnesses. Lastly, white stands for non-urgent conditions.

the community. Even though there are other safety net providers and clinics in most communities, the ED is often the only place with open doors for patients that experience substantial barriers to accessing care. (Asplin et al., 2003) like immigrants, homeless or people without insurance in private systems like US.

To tackle the issue of the management of minor codes there are two different possible solutions:

(i) Investing more in the integration between primary care and acute care preventing this type of patients to even arrive at ED through the strengthening of intermediate care solutions.
(ii) Creating dedicated separate flows for this type of patients as illustrated in the following of this Paragraph.

This latter solution can be replicated also in the case of elderly, in fact hospitals have experienced, with success, the adoption of the so called "gray" pathway dedicated to the elderly people.

ED throughput / internal processes

ED processes are plagued by other problems as well. For example, some studies have shown that shortages of nurses, junior medical staff and specialty doctors have a strong impact on crowding (Bernstein et al. 2009).

Several other factors such as poor physical design and shortage of physical space, equipment and computers, difficulties in accessing medical notes, tests, results and ancillary services, and time spent on discharging or arranging follow-up appointments are all thought to contribute to crowding (Morris et al., 2012). For example, a study (Goienetxea et al., 2017) proves that reducing by 50% the time needed for laboratory response does have an impact on the overall ED LOS by roughly 15%.

Furthermore, using staff differently and hiring additional profiles can help alleviate ED overcrowding. Hospitals could hire writers to handle documentation tasks since it is estimated that emergency physicians spend between 90 and 120 min per 8 hours on documentation. In addition, the use of mental health nurses to provide special support, social workers to help facilitate timely discharge, and patient flow coordinators to coordinate admissions, diagnostic results, and so forth, could reduce overcrowding problems in the ED.

In addition, the set-up of performance monitoring systems brings an improvement along different dimensions such as (i) triage wait time, (ii) number of admitted patients waiting more than 8 hours for a hospital bed, (iii) increase in patients discharged before the target, and decrease in ED LOS (Perera et al., 2014).

Another innovation which has proved effective in improving patient flows management has been the adoption of visual management aids (Cfr. Paragraph 4.1): in this type of models ED staff, through the help of electronic visual aids, has an immediate sense about the state of any single bed in the hospital: busy, free or patient to be discharged within the day. This solution helps smoothing patient flows from the ED and inpatient wards.

As outlined by other studies of the author (Villa 2012; Villa et al. 2014) on average in the Italian hospitals roughly 70/80% of ED cases are minor codes namely white and yellow. In this context, in order to help smoothing patient flows it is advisable to apply one of the principle of lean management (namely flows separation) and create separate settings for minor codes. As outlined in Figure 8, three are mainly three different possible organizational models:

1. Ambulatory for minor codes: Ambulatory managed by primary care doctors dedicated to white codes;
2. See and treat: A space managed by nurses for the treatment of minor pathologies;
3. Fast track: Direct access to outpatient specialties for certain clinical conditions.

Figure 7. Example of flows separation for minor codes at ED.

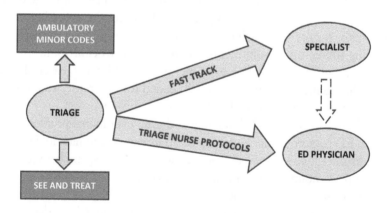

Source: authors' elaboration.

Output component

Finally, several studies have focused on the output component and have established how the inability to transfer patient to inpatient beds is the main cause of ED patient flows problems. For example, Villa and colleagues (Villa et al. 2013) have found a correlation between the ED LOS and the ratio of patients discharged by noon.

To confirm this evidence several studies show a direct link between discharge policies and ED waiting time. For example, centralization of acceptance authority for multiple medical services with one hospitalist, along with rounds in critical care areas to update shared capacity information, resulted in a decrease in hours of ED diversion and a decrease in ED LOS for patients admitted to critical care beds (Howell et al., 2008; Howell et al., 2010). Use of a bedside discharge process checklist with an afternoon planning huddle increased ED discharges before noon (DBN) and decreased ED boarding time (Beck et al., 2016). Removal of urethral catheters at midnight prior to discharge, compared to 6 am, was associated with a 163.6% increase in patients discharged later in the same day (Noble et al., 1990).

Implementation of an afternoon meeting to address discharge barriers for next-day discharge was associated with a more-than-triple increase in next day DBN, and a decrease in O/E LOS (Wertheimer et al., 2014).

Constraints are also present in discharging patients safely back in society. With a lack of community and psychiatric care and poor access to transport, the discharge process is disturbed, thus contributing to ED overcrowding (Derlet and Richards, 2000).

Other variables found in the scientific literature able to explain ED crowd are closure of nearby hospitals, lack of physicians and other providers in the community, delays in inpatient discharge or increased demand for beds (Morris et al. 2012).

ED overcrowding can be caused by several limitations of the healthcare system. For example, there is a lack of communication between the general practitioners, who are supposed to take care of the follow up, and the ED physicians, resulting in more readmissions. Many EDs complain about a lack of integration of community and hospital resources and about a lack of community care resources (Affleck et al. 2013).

The ED: natural variability vs. artificial variability

At the ED we can register fluctuations in demand caused by sources of natural variability. As said in Paragraph 1.5, natural variability cannot be eliminated but can be predicted and managed. For example, several years of data analysis of ED patient flows show recurrent trends in patient arrivals, likewise:

- The peak of arrivals is concentrated in the early morning (see Figure 8);
- The busiest day of the week is Monday (see Figure 9).

Despite such predictability in arrivals, a recent study conducted with the colleagues Marsilio, Tomas Roldan and Salmasi (Marsilio et al., 2020) show that Emergency Departments are not capable of dealing with this natural variability and peaks in arrivals determine a statistically significant increase in the overall ED length of stay.

Figure 8. Percentage ED admissions by time of day.

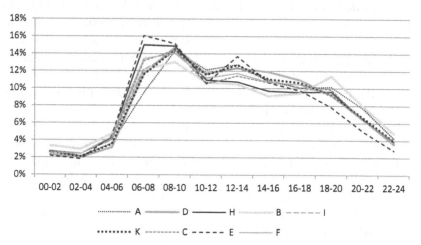

Source: Villa S. (2017) Presentation Annual Conference HEMA (Healthcare Management Association) "Redesigning Emergency Department Patient Flows: Italian benchmarking study".

Figure 9. Percentage ED admissions by weekday.

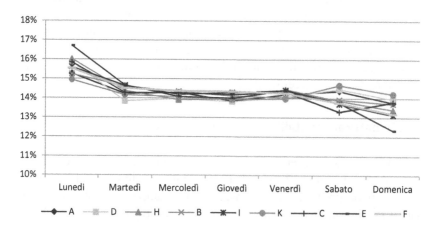

Source: Villa S. (2017) Presentation Annual Conference HEMA (Healthcare Management Association) "Redesigning Emergency Department Patient Flows: Italian benchmarking study".

2.4. The patient-centered hospital model

This Paragraph presents the patient-centered hospital model as a new process-based way of reorganizing hospital assets, particularly beds. The transition towards these new innovative models has been pushed, in the very last years, by a deep change in the epidemiological demand, namely:

1. Patients are increasingly elderly with chronic diseases and frequent co-morbidities.
2. The average nursing and clinical complexity of patients has increased.
3. Pressures on ED have significantly increased in the very last period (regardless the recent COVID-19 pandemic).

In this context, the traditional organization of hospital care based on clinical specialties and one fits-to-all settings (where patients with different clinical and nursing needs are jointly managed) is incapable of providing satisfying levels of quality of care.

Hospitals are, thereafter, increasingly looking with interest at new organizational paradigms, often labelled, in different ways such as *"the care-focused organization"* or the *"patient-centered model"* or *"the progressive patient-care model"*.

In any case, the ambition is to reshape hospital care delivery processes **around the needs of patients** and away from the traditional physicians-centered view (Lega and De Pietro, 2005; Villa et al., 2009).

This means guiding hospitals beyond the rationale (and shortcomings) of the traditional organization based on the professional bureaucracy archetype. We can no longer sustain functional self-referential designs, where resources are duplicated, economies of scale are underexploited, clinical integration and clinical governance is nonexistent, and autonomy (in using the specialty's resources) prevails over accountability (Lega, 2006 and Villa et al., 2009).

As represented in Figure 10, the challenge is to move from a vertical specialty-centered organization to a horizontal patient-centered organization where resources (e.g. nurses, outpatient clinics operating rooms and nurses) are organized in a flexible and multidisciplinary way around criteria that differ from the traditional clinical specialties (e.g. orthopedics, general surgery, sore-nose-throat surgery, ecc.).

Figure 10. Patient-Centered Hospital: from a vertical to a horizontal organizational model.

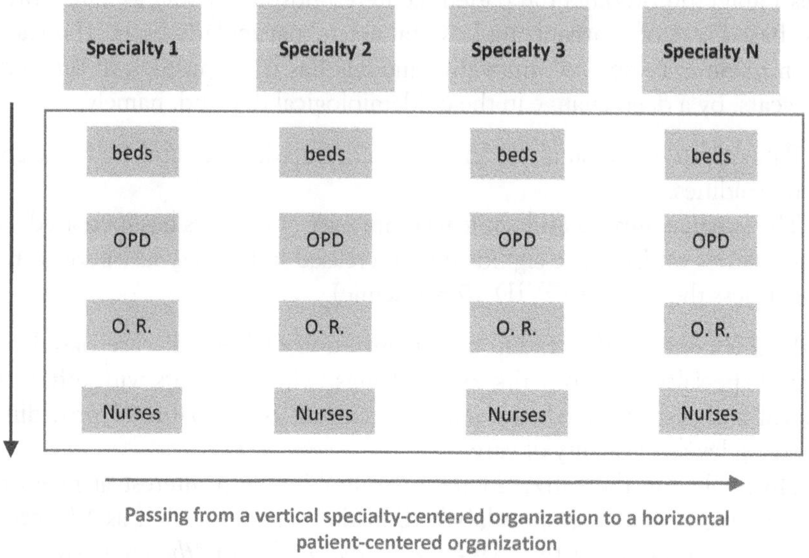

Passing from a vertical specialty-centered organization to a horizontal patient-centered organization

Source: authors' elaboration.

The concept of patient-centered hospital (or "progressive patient-care model") has been developed first in the UK (Villa, 2012) where a white paper devised by the Department of Health suggested redesigning hospital care around four different levels:

Level 3

Patients requiring advanced respiratory support alone or basic support together with support for at least 2 organ systems. This level includes all complex patients requiring support for multi-organ failure.

Level 2

Patients requiring more detailed observation or intervention, including support for a single failing organ system or post-operative care or those 'stepping down' from higher levels of care (typically called High Care or High Dependence Unit) [11].

---

[11] In UK healthcare professionals typically refer to these patients as "not too bad for ICU, not too well for regular wards". The BMC (Boston Medical Centre) case, presented in Paragraph 2.5, illustrates the functioning of a similar unit called *"step-down-unit"*.

Level 1

Patients at risk of their condition deteriorating, or those recently relocated from higher levels of care, whose needs can be met on an acute ward with additional advice and support from the critical care team.

Level 0

Patients whose needs must be met through normal care in an acute hospital.

In extreme summary, we can conclude that, according to this model, hospital care should be organized around four different levels: (i) low care; (ii) acute ordinary care; (iii) high care and (iv) critical intensive care.

However, these concepts risk being too general and vague, and so it is necessary to come up with more pragmatic criteria to redesign hospital healthcare delivery. Otherwise, we run the risk of passing from a quite orderly vertical model based on clinical specialties to a situation of chaos, as the one represented in the picture below.

"And when the music stops, grab a bed . . ."

This reminds to an old kid's game carried out with the chairs: there is a chair less (in this case a bed) so, when the music stops there is always a kid that remains without a chair and so he/she goes off the game.

In reality, there is not a unique and ideal model of patient-centered hospital. As indicated by the scientific literature (Villa et al., 2009; Villa,

2012; Gabutti et al., 2017) there are possible different criteria to reorganize wards other than clinical specialty, such as:

* *Expected length of stay*

In this case, multi-specialty wards are created for patients with similar length of stay such as:

(i)   Day surgery/day hospital area dedicated to those patients who do need a hospital bed since their diagnostic and therapeutic pathway can be concluded within the day.

(ii) Week hospitals (medical and surgical patients whose stay in the hospital is less than 5 days).

(iii) Long-stay settings dedicated to patients who need to stay in the hospital more than 14 days for different possible reasons (e.g. age, co-morbidities, complications and so on). In this case patients can arrive from different hospital settings: medical and surgical hospital areas, emergency department, or directly from the community, referred there by primary care physicians. In some cases, this area is managed autonomously by nurses and located outside hospital's walls.

(iv) Outpatient platform a separated setting dedicated to specialized visits that last in few minutes (typically less than an hour).

* *Unscheduled demand (urgency and emergency cases)*

As for the level of urgency it must be stressed that, more and more often, modern hospitals tend to keep urgent and, in general, unscheduled cases separate from elective patients (Lega and De Pietro, 2005; Litvak et al. 2005; Villa et al., 2009). Under this category, we can register experiences such as:

(i)   Urgency area for medical patients coming from the ED whose stay in the hospital is less than three days (the so-called high turn-over wards) [12].

(ii) Dedicated operating rooms and wards for unscheduled surgical patients coming from the ED.

* *The level of technology required to support patient care*

For example, the level of technology is the variable that drives the organization of intensive care units: in this case, in fact, in all hospitals, patients are sent, independently to the clinical specialty, to this department because they need mechanical ventilation systems.

---

[12] Another possible mission of these wards is to stabilize the patient and, then, redirect him/her to specialized wards (e.g. cardiology or respiratory unit).

- *Clinical complexity vs. nursing workload*

As represented in Table 6, other important drivers for reorganizing hospital wards are clinical complexity and nursing workload. Since this is not a clinical book, we will not go, in this text, into the details of the different tools to measure these two dimensions [13], but as we can see from the table below the intersection of clinical complexity and nursing workload paves the way for different possible organizational models, for example:

  o Patients clinically unstable and with a high nursing workload need to be treated in critical area units (e.g., Intensive Care Units).
  o "High Care" units typically have monitored beds and accommodate patients requiring more intensive level of nursing assistance (e.g., a ratio nurses-to-patient 3 to 1).
  o Stable patients with high nursing workload can be managed in low care settings managed autonomously by nursing personnel.

- *Age*

As confirmed by several studies (Legramante et al 2016 and Mattison, 2019) elderly behave differently at the ED (they stay longer and they are characterized by a a much worse clinical complexity) and at the hospital wards (where they often represent the so-called bed-blockers). It is, thus, possible thinking to create physical spaces dedicated to the care of elderly like the silver code area in the emergency department or the ortho-geriatric ward at the hospital, an area entirely dedicated to the surgical follow-up for orthopedic patients over 65 or 70 years.

Table 6. Clinical complexity vs. nursing workload.

NURSING WORKLOAD	CLINICAL COMPLEXITY		
	Stable Patients	Patients with risk of instability	Instable Patients
High Nursing Workload	Post Acute Care Patients Fragile Patients Frequent Users	High care	Intensive Care Units
Middle Nursing Workload	Multi-Disciplinary Wards	High care	Sub Intensive Care Units
Low Nursing Workload	Low Care DH/DS Home Care	?	

Source: authors' elaboration.

---

[13] In the scientific literature a widely used tool to measure clinical complexity is the MEWS (Modified Early Warning Score).

Figure 11 presents a classification of all the possible operational models of the patient-centered hospital on the basis of two different dimensions:

1. Throughput time that is the time needed to get the all healthcare delivery process done.
2. Type of care making a distinction between (i) day care; (ii) low care; (iii) acute care; (iv) critical care and (v) post-acute care.

The figure includes also, as possible setting, the model of focused factory, an innovative model described extensively in Paragraph 4.2 of this book.

Figure 11. Possible operational models of the patient-centered hospital.

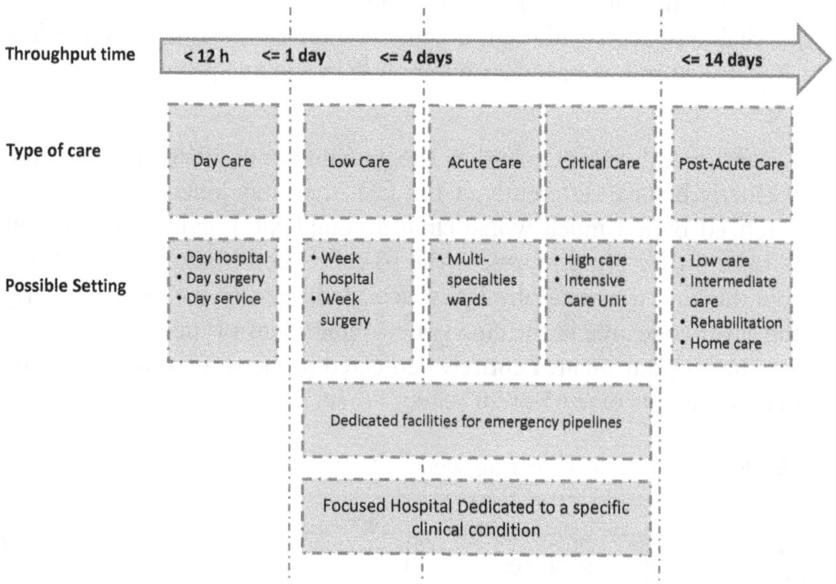

Source: authors' elaboration.

Another way of representing the possible different operational models is to make a distinction between medical and surgical patients. The separation of flows, in the case of surgical patients, is easier and can be based on either the expected length of stay (e.g., week surgery) or the type of demand (elective vs. unscheduled cases). On the contrary, in the case of medical patients it is necessary to graduate the different settings according to clinical complexity and/or nursing workload.

Figure 12. Patient-centered Hospital models for surgical and medical patients.

	Surgical Patients		Medical Patients
Level 0	Week Surgery		Low Care
			Week Hospital
Level 1	Continuous Cycle		Multi-disciplinary wards
	Urgencies		
Level 2	High Care*		
Level 3	Critical Area (intensive & sub-intensive)		

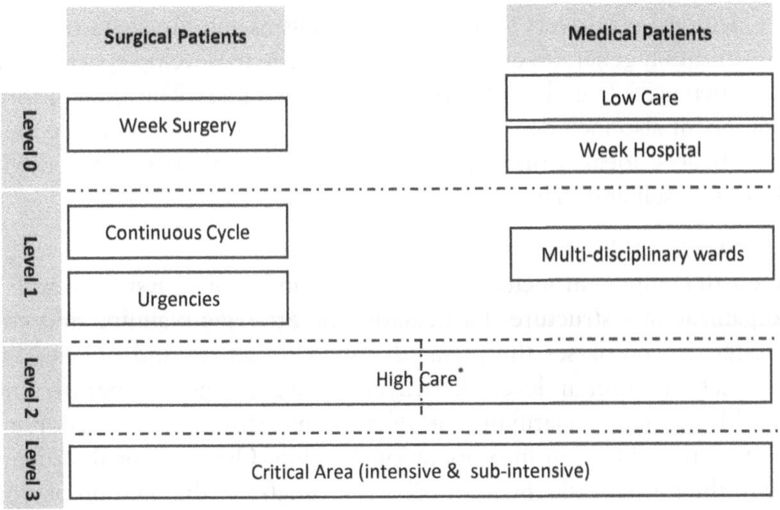

* The high care setting can be separated or shared among surgical and medical patients.
Source: authors' elaboration.

Organizational conditions

It is important, in this context, to stress the fact that transforming a hospital towards the patient-centered model is not just a simple operation of building up or tearing down some walls but it is necessary to act in coordination on all the main components of an organization particularly (see Figure 13):

1. *Primary Clinical Processes*
Core processes in health care delivery organizations consist of all the diagnosis, treatment, and assistance activities done to patients. As seen in chapter 1, a traditional tool to analyze and improve primary clinical processes is the clinical pathway, a tool designed to translate evidence-based clinical guidelines into appropriate and effective organization of core processes at the local level, targeting homogenous categories of patients.

2. *Operation Management*
As detailed throughout all this text the Operations Management can be defined as the enabling mechanism which supports production processes. More specifically, Operations Management applied to health care means managing and optimizing the flow of goods and patients across the different hospital production units through scheduling and capacity planning, organization of spaces, process design and execution, and information systems.

3. People Management

People management (or the equivalent term human resources management) includes soft drivers such as the mechanisms and processes by which the organization generates and spreads knowledge to develop specific skills and competencies (e.g., leadership, teamwork, training). This organizational component also includes the working culture that refers to people motivations, beliefs, ideas, principles, ideological assumptions associated with the hospital itself and their work.

4. Organizational Infrastructure

This fourth component includes the planning and control system as well as the organizational structure. Particularly, the Strategic planning and control system encompasses the planned system objectives and policies that hospital sets, at different levels, in delivering care and meeting performance goals with the aim of clarifying the relevant and sustainable direction and translating that direction into operational action. Organizational structure refers to the formal assignment of roles and functions, the division of work among the different units and all the mechanisms to make the hospital work (*who does what with which goals*). The organizational context also includes the information system necessary to collect the data to measure whether the goals set have been achieved.

Figure 13. Main components of a healthcare delivery organization.

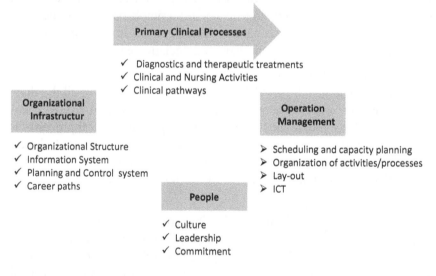

Source: authors' elaboration.

In the final part of this chapter, we try to briefly summarize the most relevant evidence, found in the scientific literature, about the impact of patient-centered hospital models on the four dimensions illustrated in Figure 13.

Primary Clinical Processes
The move towards a process-based patient-centered hospital implies redesigning the sequence of clinical activities performed to the patient and a real change of the physical spaces crossed throughout the whole cycle of care. It is, thus, very much important to define – within multidisciplinary clinical pathways – clear criteria to get IN and get OUT each single hospital setting. These criteria need to be used and monitored at the two main hospital doors: (i) Emergency Department and (ii) Outpatient Department.

Operations Management
Moving to a horizontal patient-centered organizational model requires extensive changes in patient flow logistics, likewise:

- spaces and resources need to be shared and managed jointly;
- allocations of beds and operating theatre hours to specialties should be based NOT on historical volumes or rights but on the actual needs of patients;
- wards should be organized in a flexible and multidisciplinary manner around the concept of intensity of care according to the patient needs;
- creation of a few "pool beds" that are set aside to accommodate patients who, for different reasons, fall off the forecast pathway, for example patients admitted to a week-surgery but, for some reasons, need to stay in the hospital more than 5 days (cfr. Infra);
- the hospital information system needs to provide real-time data about the status of each single bed providing information like: (i) patient's name; (ii) specialty assigned to the patient; (iii) type of setting (e.g., week surgery or high care) and (iv) the name of clinical tutor;
- hospital workload (expressed by the number of patients to be treated) needs to be smoothed and spread evenly across the days of the week.

If the patient-centered model implies a robust and well-functioning hospital operations system it is, however, worth noticing how the opposite is not necessarily always true; in fact a well-defined OM system does not necessary imply the adoption of this model but might support other models such as the focused hospital model described in Paragraph 4.4.

Organizational Infrastructure
A study conducted with the colleagues Barbieri and Lega (Villa et al., 2009) proves that the transformation towards these new innovative models im-

plies profound changes in the overall organizational infrastructure with the creation of **new organizational roles** such as:

1. The heads of the new units: High Care, Week Surgery, Week Hospital, Urgency Medicine, and Post-Acute Care;
2. Admissions coordinators in charge of the pre-recovery process and of the admission procedures;
3. Hospital rounds coordinator in charge of the coordination of the visits to the ward by the different specialties;
4. Supply coordinator in charge of managing the logistical flows of goods (pharmaceuticals, medical devices, and other materials) to the different wards;
5. Operating Room Coordinator in charge of controlling the use of the operating theatres;
6. The bed facilitator – generally a nurse – in charge of establishing efficient patient placements in the different inpatient settings. In doing so the bed facilitator collaborates with the medical staff to assess patient needs and appropriate placement of individual patients. The bed facilitator is required to use operational and clinical judgment daily to prioritize bed assignment and reassignment;
7. Clinical tutor: in charge of "following" a patient through all his/her pathway and of correctly coordinating all the activities and professionals involved in it, as well as providing constant guidance and support to the patient himself and to his/her family;
8. Operations Management function: as outlined in the previous session, the management of a patient-centered hospital needs to be backed up by a sound OM system; it is, therefore, important to create a team / unit dedicated to this area and to clearly define the system of responsibilities.

Finally, this type of models implies the development of two different types of organizational responsibilities (see Figure 14):

1. one related to the management of these new multidisciplinary horizontal platforms (e.g., day surgery, week surgery, high care) with a focus on efficiency and productivity aspects;
2. and the other one more related to appropriateness and clinical outcome with indicators such as adjusted mortality rate or re-admissions rate.

Figure 14. Double level of planning and control.

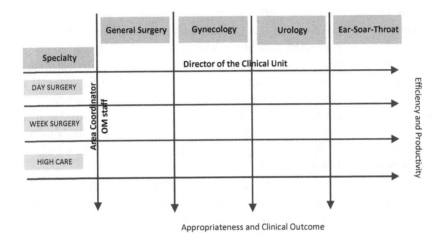

Source: authors' elaboration.

People

The transition towards these new models implies strong changes on two different categories of healthcare professionals: (i) physicians and (ii) nurses.

As for physicians, this model implies a sharp cultural change: in fact, doctors do not own, anymore, specific settings and pieces of the hospital but they need to share space with other doctors belonging to different specialties. This, eventually, also implies a reconfiguration of physicians' careers paths with a deeper emphasis on clinical results rather than managerial aspects (cfr. session dedicated to organizational infrastructure).

As for nurses it must be noted that these new organizational models rely heavily on a strong commitment from nurses who are required to take on managerial responsibilities and to deal with a wider case-mix of patients. In fact, while doctors act as specialized consultants and show up at the floor only to visit their patients, the day-by-day activity is left in the hands of nurses. Therefore, to nurture this process of change, it is necessary to heavily invest in nurse training programs both on managerial and clinical issues. In this sense, we can say that innovations in patient flow logistics have provided an opening for widening and further expanding the cultural debate about the nursing profession. The new care settings urge nurses to evolve their professionalism towards a multidisciplinary approach rather than a specialty approach. This can represent an organizational stumbling block but can also become a major field for experimenting the future development of nursing profession.

How to get things done: the case of week surgery

In my classes (executive and master level education) – to illustrate the complexity of implementing this type of changes in real life – I usually use, for teaching purposes, the case of week surgery.

Week surgery is a hospital ward dedicated to elective surgical patients who are expected to have a surgical follow-up of less than five days. It is a multidisciplinary/multi-specialties ward which closes Friday night (or, at the latest, Saturday morning). In this unit, beds are assigned randomly and with flexibility way to the various surgical specialties that use this area. Generally, week surgery encompasses all the surgical specialties including Orthopedics and Gynecology [14].

The figure below tries to summarize this effort by classifying the different organizational conditions along the four components described earlier: (i) primary clinical processes; (ii) Operations Management; (iii) people management and (iv) organizational infrastructure.

As represented in Figure 15 such innovations have a significant impact on the hospital operational system, particularly it is necessary to:

– Reorganize hospital lay-out to create a brand-new ward dedicated to the week surgery patients.
– Create a pool of beds next to the week surgery to accommodate patients that cannot be discharged by Friday night.
– Centralize and standardize the pre-admission testing; in fact, it is important that patients arrive at the day of the surgery "ready to go" with all the tests done and set.
– Change of the OR scheduling system especially at weekly level; in fact, in order to discharge patients by Friday, it is important to schedule procedures that require two-three days of surgical follow-up at the beginning of the week.
– Invest in the ICT system in order to have real-time information about the status of each single bed regarding, for example (i) name of the patient; (ii) specialty and clinical tutor; (iii) day or hour of possible discharge.

---

[14] Highly specialized specialties (such as neurosurgery or cardiac surgery) do not typically use this particular setting.

Figure 15. Organizational conditions for the implementation of patient-centered hospital models.

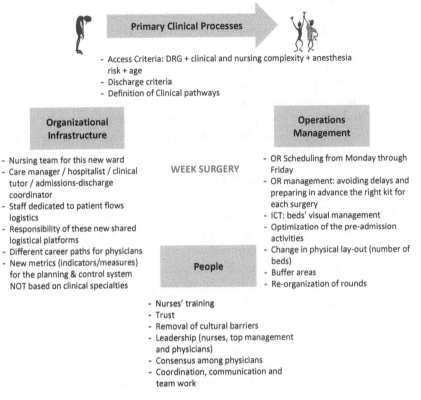

Primary Clinical Processes

- Access Criteria: DRG + clinical and nursing complexity + anesthesia risk + age
- Discharge criteria
- Definition of Clinical pathways

Organizational Infrastructure

- Nursing team for this new ward
- Care manager / hospitalist / clinical tutor / admissions-discharge coordinator
- Staff dedicated to patient flows logistics
- Responsibility of these new shared logistical platforms
- Different career paths for physicians
- New metrics (indicators/measures) for the planning & control system NOT based on clinical specialties

WEEK SURGERY

Operations Management

- OR Scheduling from Monday through Friday
- OR management: avoiding delays and preparing in advance the right kit for each surgery
- ICT: beds' visual management
- Optimization of the pre-admission activities
- Change in physical lay-out (number of beds)
- Buffer areas
- Re-organization of rounds

People

- Nurses' training
- Trust
- Removal of cultural barriers
- Leadership (nurses, top management and physicians)
- Consensus among physicians
- Coordination, communication and team work

Source: authors' elaboration.

The impact of patient-centered hospitals

Despite the growing interest in these topics (Villa et al., 2009; Gabutti and al., 2017) there seem to be several "gaps" in what is known about the actual impact of this type of innovation in the organization of hospital care.

With the colleagues Barbieri and Lega (Villa et al., 2019) we have analyzed the impact of the transition to this new model of care in three different hospitals, finding some common robust trends along the following lines:

- The new way of organizing care allows to concentrate scarce resources on the patients with the highest clinical and nursing needs.
- Patients are no longer parked in areas where they cannot receive appropriate care (known as "trolley waits").

- The actual sharing of space among different clinicians stimulates a fruitful exchange of knowledge and information[15]; in this perspective, the logistical integration has been both the "constrain" and the necessary element for life in common that has created room and opportunity for integration.
- Thanks to a more flexible and appropriate utilization of assets, equipment, and human resources[16] all the three hospitals analyzed in the study have gained significant increase in hospital productivity in terms of (i) reduction in average hospital length of stay; (ii) increase in beds' occupancy rate; (iii) increase in hospital case-mix complexity and (iv) reduction of turn-over ratio.

Furthermore, other studies (Orlandi et al., 2006; De Pietro et al., 2011) have reported an increased patient satisfaction, especially about the identification of a medical and/or nursing tutor. Patients report also to no longer being "parked" in areas where they cannot receive adequate care.

In any case, it is, now, important to define a set of shared and standard indicators to measure the actual impact of the implementation of this new model and to analyze possible gaps compared to expected goals in a continuous quality improvement perspective. It is, thus, very much relevant:

1. Monitoring the effects of changes in terms of trends of production mix, productivity, level of appropriateness, and quality of care delivered.
2. Checking compliance with admission and discharge criteria for the various patient care settings: these new systems work well, in fact, only if patients move smoothly along the cycle of care receiving care and assistance in the most appropriate setting[17].

---

[15] The paper written with Barbieri and Lega (Villa et al., 2009) quotes the words of an ear, nose and throat specialist that, I believe, well represents this concept *"... with this new logistical model, I have the chance to share facts and experiences that helped me in my daily clinical activity with other colleagues. With the previous model I could only see the other specialists briefly, and by chance, in the hospital cafeteria ..."*.

[16] In Operations Management terminology, this redesign has moved the process from a "long and thin" structure to a "short and fat" structure, which is much more flexible.

[17] For example, the case of BMC, described in Chapter 2.5, illustrates patient flow problems in the use of the step-down unit, an area where patients tend to stay longer than appropriate because of lack of clear criteria to get in and out.

2.5. Improving Quality through redesign of hospital patient flow logistics: the case of Boston Medical Centre (BMC) [18]

The case, illustrated in this paragraph, can be effectively used in class to illustrate the application, in a real setting, of models and tools for the analysis and redesign of hospital patient flow logistics.

In 2003 the Boston Medical Center (BMC) was suffering from a series of problems that were seriously threatening its good reputation as multi-specialties community hospital devoted to serve indistinctly the whole community of Boston area, and creating increasing levels of dissatisfaction among patients and families.

At that time in fact the hospital was plagued by problems such as stressful working climate, patients accommodated in inappropriate settings causing lack of beds, Emergency Department (ED) overcrowding and diversions, elective surgical cases bumped or postponed.

In the following years, BMC was able to fix all these problems through innovative and relatively simple changes in patient flow logistics such as the set-up of a separated path for emergency cases, the extensive revision of scheduling and flow procedures, and the creation of new organizational roles to better support patients flow management.

These changes made BMC a world-wide recognized best-practice in the management of patient flows, but, at the beginning, implementing the new system was everything but simple and straightforward for hospital management and physicians. In the words of BMC bed facilitator Registered Nurse Janet Gorman … *"You look back and say, why did we ever live with it? I mean it was such an easy thing to fix, why didn't we think of fixing it before? I think in medicine we don't look at the obvious"*.

Boston Medical Center: New England's largest trauma center

In 2003 Boston Medical Center (BMC) was a private, not-for-profit, 623-

---

[18] This case has been built around my experience as intern at Boston Medical Center in the period July - December 2003 within the Program for Management of Variability in Healthcare Delivery Boston University within the Urgent Matters program (a national initiative sponsored by Robert Wood Johnson Foundation). Relevant information and data have been gathered also in publications in scientific journals, newspapers articles and web sites (reported in the References), part is drawn by interviews administered to people working at BMC. A special thanks goes to Prof. Eugene Litvak (former Director of the Program for the Management of Variability in Health Care Delivery at Boston University Health Policy Institute); Prof. Joseph Restuccia (Professor of Operations and Technology Management, Boston University – School of Management); Dr. John Chessare (former Chief Medical Officer at BMC); Janet Gorman (Bed Facilitator, BMC); Robert Brogna (Program Manager, Operational Improvement, BMC). An edited version of the case has been also published within the European Cases Clearing House (Villa and Fattore, 2008).

bed, academic medical center with a community-based focus. Established in July 1996, Boston Medical Center was the first full asset merger of a public hospital (Boston City Hospital) with a private academic medical center (Boston University Medical Center Hospital) ever happened in the whole Massachusetts State. In 2003 Boston Medical Center had nearly 5,000 employees, more than 1,000 physicians and an annual operating budget of roughly $2.0 billion. Boston Medical Center was the major teaching affiliate for Boston University Schools of Medicine and Dental Medicine.

Although a private institution, Boston Medical Center was still able to fulfill the role of "safety net" to Boston's poor and uninsured, providing more than $350 million in free care (care offered without any charge).

With nearly 28,000 admissions and more than 700,000 outpatient visits annually, Boston Medical Center provided a comprehensive range of inpatient and outpatient services in more than 70 areas of medical specialties and subspecialties, including cardiac care and surgery, hypertension, neurological care, oncology, orthopedics, geriatrics and women's health. With the largest 24-hour Level I trauma center in New England [19], BMC Emergency Department had more than 124,000 visits each year (for more data on BMC activities see Table 7).

Table 7. BMC general info (fiscal year 2003).

Licensed Beds		Occupancy Rate (of staffed beds)	80%
Medicine/Surgery*	361	Discharges	27,616
Obstetrics/Gynecology	20		
Intensive and Coronary Care	62	Outpatient Activity	
Neonatal Intensive Care	15	Outpatient Clinic Visits	421,828
Pediatric Intensive Care	4	Outpatient Ancillary Visits	283,495
Pediatrics	22	Emergency Department Visits	124,447
Rehabilitation	24	Ambulatory Surgery	20,832
Chronic Care	100	Outpatient Observation	4,991
Psychiatry	15		
Total	623	Physicians	1,079
Average Length of Stay		Residents and Fellows	626
Medical/Surgical Acute	5.60 days		
Acute Rehabilitation	23.58 days	Nurses	1,454
Newborn (includes NICU)	4.51 days		
		Employees	
		Full-time equivalent employees	4,728

* The surgical area includes the following main specialties: (i) Orthopedics and Trauma; (ii) Cardiac surgeries; (iii) Vascular surgeries; (iv) General surgery; (v) Pediatric surgery. The medical area includes: (i) Cardiology; (ii) Oncology and (iii) General Medicine.
Source: adapted from Villa S. and Fattore G. (2008).

---

[19] For New England we intend the northeast area of the United States. This area includes six States: Maine, New Hampshire, Massachusetts, Vermont, Connecticut and Rhode Island.

In 2003 the BMC layout was organized around two separate areas: Menino Pavilion (8 operating rooms) and Newton Pavilion (12 operating rooms). In all, BMC's operating rooms used to deal with more than 15,000 cases each year (for more data on Operating Rooms see Table 8).

Table 8. Operating Rooms' statistics.

Measure	Newton	Menino
N. Operating Rooms	12	8
N. daily cases	30-35	25-32
N. yearly cases	8.601	6.608
Cancellation Rate	10%	20%
Daily Add-On cases	1-2	5-10
Week-end cases	0-4	2-20
Special services offered	Cardiac Surgery, Ophthalmology	Pediatrics, Trauma, Hyperbaric Chambers

Source: adapted from Villa S. and Fattore G. (2008).

At Boston Medical Center floors were organized into Patient Care Units (PCU), each with 30 beds. A nurse manager had overall responsibility for each Unit, with the assistance of a case manager who coordinated all clinical activities performed on the patients, kept track of all patient information, and managed relationships with patients' families. Except for orthopedics and cardiac surgery, the PCUs were managed in a multi-disciplinary and flexible manner according to the criteria that it was the physician who followed the patient, and not the other way around.

There was also a special PCU called Step-Down Unit where patients who needed a higher level of nursing care were located. In this area the nurse-patients ratio was 1 to 3 (while, on average, at BMC the ratio was equal to 1 to 5). There were no monitored beds, and patients who needed special technological assistance were sent to the Intensive Care Units (ICU). Three different types of patients could have access to the Step-Down Unit: (i) surgical patients; (ii) medical patients and (iii) patients coming directly from the Emergency Department (ED). The length of stay varied from 1 day to 13 days with an average of about two days.

Finally, there were two rehabilitative and post-acute care Units: (i) acute rehabilitative area (18 beds) and (ii) transitional care area (12 beds). The latter was an area dedicated mainly to the care of the elderly.

2003: serious problems at Boston Medical Center

During the year 2003, the management at BMC was facing a particularly complicated situation at the Emergency Department. Far too often BMC had to close its ED and consequently divert patients (most of the time in need of urgent and critical care) to other more distant and less specialized hospitals[20]. Furthermore, the Emergency Department was deservedly building a reputation of always being overcrowded with patients experiencing unacceptably long waits before receiving care. It appeared that BMC was suffering from its inability to deal with demand that overwhelmed its available capacity. Surgeons complained about a related problem that patients scheduled for elective surgeries were often "bumped" off the schedule because incoming emergencies were assigned to their operating room (OR).

At the Menino Pavilion the cancellation rate for surgical cases was equal to 15-20% for blocked times. At BMC each specialty and each surgeon had its own OR block time assigned in advance. For example, cardiac surgery might have its operating room time on Monday (8 a.m. to 7 p.m.) and Wednesday (8 a.m. to 2 p.m.). At BMC, if, for any reason, the time available was not fully used there was no way to reallocate the time to other surgeons or other specialties. On average, 1/3 (about 10 patients per day) and sometimes ½ of all surgical activity consisted of unscheduled cases with serious problems in the normal OR operations (preparing the patients, setting up the room, and so on).

This circumstance made any planning attempt very difficult, making everything much more difficult to manage. As pointed out by the Chief Medical Officer of BMC, Doctor John Chessare:

"The constant state of unpredictability of working conditions is a source of stress and stress is the main cause of errors."
"Imagine what this means – explained the head of the cardiac surgery Unit, Doctor Oz Shapira - for a patient getting ready for an open-heart surgery and having been told that the surgery has been postponed. An awful experience to recommend to somebody, one that also has negative effects on the activities of surgeons and nurses and, on top of everything, it seriously threatens the quality and safety of care offered to the patients".

This was happening in one out of every five elective cases at Menino Pavilion. For example, during the period April – September 2003, 334 elective surgeries had been bumped because of the arrival of 157 cases coming from

---

[20] The issue of ED overcrowding has been particularly pressing in Massachusetts, where one-third of EDs have closed since 1981 and hospitals routinely divert ambulances to other medical centers because they cannot handle more patients (Allen S., "Emergency Room Recovery" The Boston Globe July, 8 2004).

ED. Despite these problems, according to the data available to BMC Chief Medical Officer at Menino Pavilion, the OR utilization rate was only 50%.

In addition, BMC was experiencing a structural shortage of nurses and high turnover. Nurses complained about the excessive workload and the continuous necessity to work over time. BMC's senior management was having a very hard time understanding the causes of the problems and identifying effective strategies to improve the situation. The hospital was under a lot of pressure because of the continuous attention of the media, which were particularly interested in problems such as queues, waiting time, ED diversions and cancellations. These problems were seriously threatening the image of the hospital and were creating dissatisfaction among patients and families.

Hence, there was an urgent need to identify and implement effective solutions to these problems. BMC was no longer able to effectively carry out its traditional role of a high specialty safety-net hospital for the poor and uninsured patients living in the New England area and, at the same time, affluent and well insured citizens of Boston were shifting to the numerous other hospital structures present in the Boston area.

Elaine Ullian, BMC's Chief Executive Officer was feeling pressure, in particular from Thomas Menino, the Mayor of Boston, who was asking for quick and dramatic changes. According to the Mayor "... *Bostonians, regardless of their income and social status, should benefit from the presence of a safety net hospital able to provide timely, safe and cost-effective care*".

Doctor Chessare had already started to mobilize the leadership of the hospital to redesign flow.

Dr Chessare, an Italian American, was a graduate of the University of Rome School of Medicine and the School of Public Health of the University of Michigan. After a long career as a practicing physician in academic medical centers with publications in the areas of child development, pediatric health services deliveries and clinical epidemiology, he firmly believed that, to achieve a world class health care, it was necessary to change the way hospitals operations were managed. He really cared about the future of Boston Medical Center, about the people working at the hospital and, finally, about the hundreds of people that every day came to BMC to get care. He was convinced that, with the support and collaboration of the whole staff (surgeons, clinicians, nurses and administrative staff), it would be possible to fix the system providing better and safer care to the patients and improving the working conditions at the hospital. Quoting a phrase by Donald M. Berwick (President and CEO, Institute for Healthcare Improvement) Dr. Chessare used to say that: "*We have to bring the science of management back into health care*".

To help address these issues, in a systematic manner, Dr. Chessare enlisted the help of Professor Eugene Litvak. Eugene Litvak, PhD was a co-founder and director of the *Program for the Management of Variability in Health Care Delivery* at the Boston University Health Policy Institute (http://www.bu.edu/mvp/). He was also a Professor at the Boston University School of Management and Adjunct Professor at Harvard School of Public Health. Litvak was an industrial efficiency expert from the former Soviet Union where he received his doctorate in Operations Research from the Moscow Institute of Physics and Technology in 1977. Before emigrating to the U.S. in 1988, he worked at the then-Soviet Ministry of Transportation. There, he helped to streamline building of the nation's railroads. When Litvak came to the U.S., he turned his sights on health care – against the advice of his American scientist friends. But Litvak was eager for a challenge so since 1995 he had been leading the development and practical applications of innovative variability methodology for cost reduction and quality improvement in health care delivery systems.

With the help of Professor Litvak doctor Chessare determined three main priorities:

1. optimize the management of urgent/emergency cases;
2. re-organize the entire OR scheduling process;
3. improve the patient flow within the hospital (particularly the chaotic flow of patients to and from the Step-Down-Unit).

Differentiated path for urgent surgical cases

Dr. Chessare received guidance from Prof. Litvak to establish a separated pathway for people who needed surgery in an urgent and consequently unplanned way. According to Dr. Chessare, it really did not make sense for a hospital with a trauma center of critical importance to all New England to be without operating rooms (ORs) entirely dedicated to patients needing unplanned surgery, most of whom coming from the ED. Without them, the OR needed to continuously revise its schedule to accommodate cases coming from the ED. Whenever a new case came from the ED, it was necessary to take a time slot in the schedule for elective surgery. Therefore, elective cases were bumped or postponed, and nurses were required to work overtime increasing cost and stress for the entire workforce.

Furthermore, as it was always impossible to free up an OR slot immediately, urgent cases were required to stay in the ED waiting for one to free up. This in turn prevented the ED from accepting new incoming patients until the patients waiting for surgery went to the OR.

Dr. Chessare decided to begin the project at the Menino Pavilion: *"We need only to decide how many operating rooms we should dedicate to the un-scheduled cases. One, I think, should be enough but we need to model different possible scenarios before making such an important decision."*

Dr. Chessare also suspected that the space dedicated to urgent cases could be used inappropriately by surgeons: cases which were not urgent (that can be safely postponed by 24 hours or more) could be disguised as urgent, thus overloading the OR that was supposed to be entirely dedicated to urgent cases. To address this problem, he created a team (including all the chiefs of the various surgical specialties, plus the chief of Anesthesia and the Chief of Emergency Medicine) charging it with the task of developing explicit and objective criteria to classify urgent cases.

Recently Chessare had discovered that a nearby hospital was using a set of criteria to define the level of urgency of surgical cases:

1. Emergency: cases to be done within 30 minutes;
2. Urgent: cases to be done between 30 minutes to 4 hours;
3. Semi-urgent: cases to be done between 4 hours to 24 hours;
4. Non urgent: cases that can be easily postpone after 24 hours.

OR planning and the issue of variability

According to the vision of BMC's top management, creating a dedicated path for emergent and urgent cases would solve the problems related to the high cancellation rate of scheduled cases. However, it was not clear whether this measure would also address the problems of ED overcrowding and diversion.

Professor Litvak and his team formulated the hypothesis that the issue of overcrowding in the ED was not solely an ED issue. Using the approach of the root-cause analysis (a quite well-known Quality Improvement Technique) they started to ask simple questions in order to go back to the real root causes of the ED problems:

Q) Why are people waiting for several hours in the waiting room?
A) Because all of the ED beds are full.

Q) Why are the ED beds full?
A) Because there aren't any Intensive Care Unit (ICU) beds available for the ED patients who need to be admitted.

Q) Why aren't there any beds available in the ICU?
A) Because they are full of patients who had scheduled surgery earlier in the day.

The data about the schedule of elective cases showed that there were huge peaks in demand, especially on Wednesdays and Thursdays, which seemed to have no logical explanation. It turned out that competition for elective surgery space was most intense on these two days. Vascular and cardiac surgeons, for example, booked almost all of their elective cases in the middle of the week with the peak on Wednesdays (see Figure 16).

Figure 16. Interventional cardiology patients: average number of cases for day of the week.

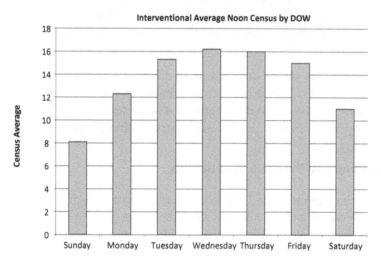

Source: "Project for Smoothing Patient Flow to Floor 6N," Program for Management of Variability in Health Care delivery, Boston University Health Policy Institute, February 2005.

More generally, in addition to the problem related to the concentration of surgeries on particular days of the week, the distribution of cases at BMC was characterized by high levels of variability. Figure 17 shows, for instance, data on census (average daily number of patients) at East 6 Newton floor (noon and midnight).

Figure 17. Census East 6 Newton floor (noon and mid-night).

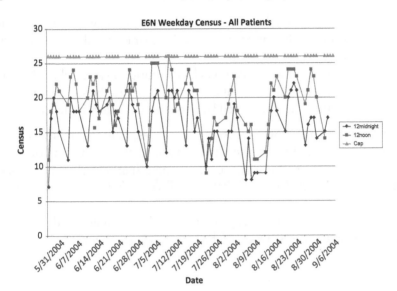

Source: "Project for Smoothing Patient Flow to Floor 6N," Program for Management of Variability in Health Care delivery, Boston University Health Policy Institute, February 2005.

There was reason to believe that this high variability in the number of elective cases performed was related to the fact that surgeons were scheduling the OR time assigned to them according to their commitments outside the hospital (patient visits in their offices, scientific conferences, courses, academic duties or, more simply, long weekend and periods of vacation). Because of this behaviour, the OR, and consequently the floors and the nurses, were overloaded in some days while idle in others.

To address these problems, Doctor Chessare cautiously approached the chiefs, starting with the vascular and cardiothoracic surgery departments, and asked the following question: "*Will you schedule your surgeries more evenly throughout the week, if we can prove that you will be able to perform more cases?*".

The surgeons, after quite a long discussion and bargaining process, eventually accepted the idea only with the promise that if the changes did not work, they would be allowed to revert to the previous system.

According to Jim Menzoian, MD, Chief of Vascular Surgery: "*I have to admit I didn't like the idea in the beginning, because, you know, we're doctors, and we don't like people telling us what to do*". But Menzoian told Chessare that "*we want to be team players*" so the surgeons changed their schedule.

The first two big changes were the following:

1. The OR block time allocation was modified, by moving, for example, some surgeons to Friday (a day typically characterized by a low occupancy rate)[21].
2. The hospital introduced a cap on elective surgical cases, which had the surgical schedulers moving patients to days where there were openings in the schedule. This eliminated large peaks and valleys in demand.

By smoothing the flow of complex surgeries, Boston Medical Center was evening out the flow of post-surgical patients thus alleviating the pressure on the most crowded areas of the hospital (particularly the Intensive Care Units and Step-Down Units) and allowing better control of beds management.

With the changes in the OR planning and the opening of a differentiated path for urgent cases, Doctor Chessare was sure *"...we'll be able to fix all our problems without any additional cost"*.

Optimizing patient flow at BMC: the complicated issue of the Step-Down Unit

As previously mentioned, floors at BMC were managed according to a multi-disciplinary approach. However, a recent innovation in the logistic and organizational hospital model of care was represented by the creation of a multi-disciplinary area called Step-Down Unit, accommodating patients who, regardless of their specific pathology, need special and more intensive nursing, but not technological assistance.

After years of training and practice, nurses became skilled at dealing with a vast range of pathologies and diseases. However, this floor was always overcrowded and there were not explicit admission and discharge criteria detailing who should be eligible for the Step-Down Unit and when a patient was considered ready to be discharged from the Unit. The situation was chaotic; in the words of Janet Gorman (Step Down Unit Nurse Manager) *"... certain days of the week it could be really a disaster. There would be patients in the surgical intensive care, in the ED and in the medical area fighting for the same beds ... So on those days of the week it was chaotic here"*.

Janet Gorman was also supporting Dr. Chessare in his attempt of optimizing the overall patient flows within the hospital. The whole hospital was

---

[21] For example, heart surgeon Shapira shifted his office hours by one day, to Thursday, to free up Fridays for operations (The Online News Hour's, 2005).

in fact plagued by serious problems in the management of patient flow, particularly in the movement of patients between the different floors and Units.

Janet Gorman was fascinated by the arguments and theories of Professor Litvak and, on a voluntary basis, in her spare time, she offered her support to the Russian Professor in collecting and analyzing data.

Doctor Chessare learnt about two innovative organizational solutions implemented by other hospitals that could help BMC in improving and streamlining its patient flow:

1. the new organizational role of Bed Facilitator;
2. the use of patient tracking software (BMC built its own version called "Bed Board") specifically designed to handle the flow of patients within hospitals.

The Bed Facilitator had both clinical and managerial competencies. Particularly, the bed facilitator worked in conjunction with all disciplines, and had responsibilities which included prioritization and assignment of all in-patients, observation and surgical day care patients to inpatient beds, established and maintained a systematic review and assessment of bed availability, ensured appropriate assignment based on clinical need and staffing constraints, worked with other departments in establishing standards for appropriate utilization of beds (inclusive of pre-operative days and direct admissions).

To assist the Bed Facilitator, BedBoard displayed real-time information on the status of every bed and patient within the hospital. This software, which could be set up on the hospital intranet, depicted all the beds present in the hospital. Thanks to this program it was possible to keep each bed in the hospital under control. The software in fact offered up-to-date information on the status of the bed: (i) bed occupied; (ii) bed free but dirty; (iii) bed available. Furthermore, it was possible to program the computer system to beep a housekeeper automatically whenever a room was free; that alone shaved off half an hour of lag time.

All the information offered by the software was available on every hospital computer. Through this software, floors could signal to the ED and to the personnel working at the Step Down Unit that there were beds available precluding the need for nurse managers to call every time the floors in search of a bed available.

Conclusions

At the end of 2003, several plans and programs were in place at BMC. Dr. Chessare was perfectly aware he was dealing with a difficult challenge but something urgent needed to be done: ED overcrowding and diversions, bumped cases and patients allocated in inappropriate settings could not be tolerated any more. He was confident on the goodness of Litvak's ideas about smoothing variability and streamlining patient flows through hospital settings, but he had still some concerns:

(i)   will we be able to provide all the data and statics to support their thesis and plans?
(ii)   will we be able to convince nurses and physicians to actually change the way scheduling and flow procedures were currently executed at BMC?
(iii) finally, and most importantly, will all these changes really help the hospital to provide a more efficient, appropriate, timely, and safer care to all its patients?

Possible questions for class discussion

The BMC case can be successfully used as a teaching case in graduate and executive classes. A possible teaching strategy is to structure the class discussion along these three questions:

1. What are the problems that were afflicting BMC in 2013?
2. Using the focusing matrix described in chapter 2 evaluate the different possible solutions available to the CMO to fix hospital problems.
3. Develop a detailed change plan to overcome the problematic situation.

NOTES
    In the design of the change plan, students can be encouraged to use the four logistical drivers illustrated in Paragraph 1.4.
    In the decision of the number of ORs to assign to emergency/urgency cases, it is possible to refer to the queueing model described in Chapter 4.6.

2.6. Sasso hospital – Reorganizing hospital wards around intensity of care: how & why?

The case, illustrated in this paragraph, can be effectively used in class to understand the most relevant organizational conditions to implement patient-centred hospital models.
First meeting with General Manager
    Dr. Veloci, General Manager of Sasso hospital, saw a unique opportunity in the guidelines put forward by the PAL (Local Implementation Plan) – the opportunity to radically change the organizational model inside Sasso hospital. The PAL was very clear: in three years' time, all the hospitals in

the area were required to re-organize hospital floors following a model based on intensity of care.

Dr. Veloci had been in charge of Sasso hospital for 4 years (See Table 2.9 for a short description of the hospital), and had one more year before his term expired. Dr. Veloci, however, wished to gain a second term, and he needed some visible results to prove the effectiveness of his leadership.

Table 9. Sasso Hospital: some data.

HOSPITAL BEDS			ORDINARY ADMISSIONS		
Regular Hospital Wards	271			**v. a.**	**%**
Critical Area	26		TOT.	**18.637**	100%
Day Hospital	35		DRG Surgical	8,759	47%
Emergency Medicine Ward	12		DRG Medical	9,878	53%
Emergency Department Observation Unit (OU)	14				
EMERGENCY DEPARTMENT			**EFFICIENCY DATA**		
Admissions per year	59.130		Bed occupancy rate*	99,6%	
Daily average	162		Bed turnover rate**	71,81	
% hospitalizations	19,8%		Average lenght of stay	6,7	
% observation unit	8,5		- DRG Surgical	5,1	
			- DRG Medical	7,5	
TYPE OF DISCHARGE	**A. V.**	**%**			
Death	808	4,2			
Ordinary discharges	16.362	87,6			
Protected discharge	242	1,3			
To other service within same facility	341	1,8			
To other facility	864	4,5			
To Rehabilitation	20	0,6			
TOT.	**18.637**	**100,0**			
* (days of stay) / (number of beds x 365)					
** (annual inpatient cases) / beds					

Source: authors' elaboration.

Dr. Veloci, therefore, decided to call a meeting with the Medical Director (Dr. Paino), one medical doctor from the Hospital Directorate (Dr. Salerno), the Director of Nursing Services (Dr. Norsi), the Quality Manager (Dr. Demingo), and the person in charge of Management control (Dr. Costa).

Veloci had a clear vision. At the meeting he said:

"... I don't want to lose time, I want us to be the first hospital in the area to 'go' intensity of care – I want to go from the old model, based on specialities, to the new one, based on intensity of care, in six months. I have sketched this plan and we will follow it ..." (see Figure 18).

Figure 18. Re-organization plan for hospital floors.

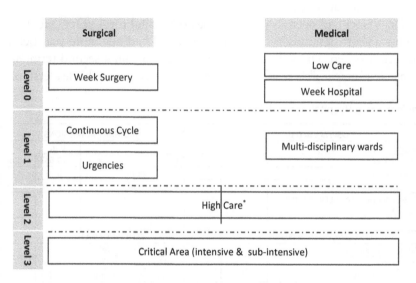

Source: authors' elaboration.

"… Dr. Norsi is going to be team coordinator. I have also in mind to start, later on, four more focus groups that are going to work on four different issues":

1. Clinical pathways – Percorsi Diagnostici Terapeutici ed Assistenziali (PDTA).
2. Patient flows logistics.
3. People.
4. Organizational structure.

> *Dr. Demingo will coordinate the PDTA group, Dr. Norsi will be in charge of groups 2 and 3, and our controller will deal with group 4.*
> *I am not particular about the strategy you are going to use; I only care about results. We will meet next month to check our progress …*
> *Now, I need to go. I have a meeting at the Regional Council.*

First meeting of PDTA (clinical pathways) group.

Dr. Demingo had several years' experience in PDTA analysis and implementation – first as consultant and then working in a university hospital bigger than Sasso.

However, the issue of clinical pathways inside a hospital based on intensity of care is quite new; it is a fascinating, as well as challenging and thorny issue.

When he took part in the meeting with Dr. Veloci, Demingo had just finished working on a pathway for respiratory failure and he, therefore, thought it was best to start from this framework to understand how diagnostic, cure and care pathways might be changed according to a model based on intensity of care.

Given the tight deadline set by the General Manager, Demingo immediately called a meeting with the Head Physicians of:

- Pulmonology.
- Intensive care.
- Medicine.
- Cardiology.
- Anaesthesiologist.

Dr. Demingo prepared quite a long and complex presentation. However, as soon as he put the key inside the USB socket of his laptop, the Head physician of Pulmonology started speaking and literally flooded Demingo with criticism:

"What is the real objective of this meeting? Talk about some illusive reorganization of care process just because some Mr.-Know-it-All working at the Local Health Authority, someone who has never set foot inside a hospital ward, has written that hospitals must be organized according to a model based on intensity of care? This kind of proposals, falling from above, is not to my taste, especially when there is no real evidence supporting its effectiveness in terms of lives saved or clinical results. I've spoken to some colleagues from the Carini Region - they have already started in this direction: the model suggested requires to discontinue the traditional organizational model based on specialities, thus erasing the identity of the different wards, these are going to be turned into big areas supported by the work of nursing staff who are trained to deal with the organizational side of beds. I don't like this model at all."

The Head physician of Cardiology, a well-known doctor and vice-president of his professional association, followed suit:

"I completely agree: the present model allows doctors to develop in-depth skills and experience on a specific organ or human apparatus, this way it is possible to take care of a patient suffering from conditions related to that specific context with maximum expertise. What is going to happen to those same doctors in a process-based hospital, or, more generally, in a hospital based on intensity of care?".

The well-respected head of General Medicine, an authority in his field, echoed his colleagues:

"Besides research, what are the advantages for our citizen-customer? We always speak about putting him at the core of our work. As far as I am

concerned, patients are dragged from one setting to the other without anyone taking charge. I have heard about new roles, for instance the clinical tutor[22] but there are some questions I'd like to ask: how can a tutor interface with patients and give him or her the care in some field where he has no expertise whatsoever? And what about legal liability?".

Dr. Demingo was utterly bewildered by such unexpected flow of criticism. More than 2 hours had passed since the start of the meeting, so he decided to go straight to the core of his presentation:

"Dear colleagues, let's try to reach some results. Let's put the patient at the core of the model and then we'll try to see how the care process changes. I am suggesting we use this methodology that I'm sure will be useful for our next meeting."

Figure 19. Breathing failure patient pathway in the patient-centred care model.

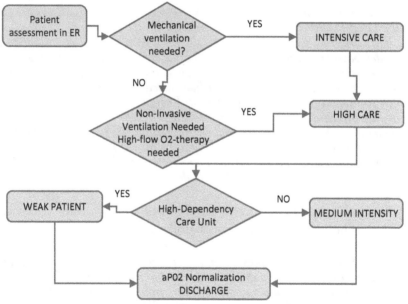

Source: authors' elaboration.

---

[22] The medical tutor (i) is the reference point for patients and their families during their stay; (ii) plans and checks the Diagnostics, treatment and care pathway agreed with the director of the Operative Unit; (iii) keeps contact with physicians from General Medicine and patients' families.

Demingo, then, showed a simplified representation of the care process for respiratory failure inside an hypothetical hospital organized according to the model presented by the General Manager (see Figure 19).

The Sasso case represents a useful teaching tool to explore pros, cons and organizational conditions of patient-centered models. The class discussion can be organized around these six questions:

1. Using, at least, three keywords, how would you define the leadership style used by Dr. Veloci?
2. What are the reasons that led Dr. Veloci to choose the model based on intensity of care? Are there any other reasons that should lead him to choose this model?
3. Focus on Dr. Veloci's leadership style and motivation for change. What are the advantages and disadvantages of such an approach?
4. What are the organizational conditions needed to implement this model?
5. What kind of indicators is important to measure to evaluate the quality and effectiveness of the model (make reference also to the clinical pathway depicted in Figure 19)?
6. How can we involve staff in the change management process? Which are the pros and cons of the change management process lead by the CEO?

Chapter 3
HEALTHCARE SUPPLY CHAIN MANAGEMENT

SUMMARY: 3.1. Definition of supply chain management in healthcare. – 3.2. Innovation trends. – 3.3. Measuring supply chain performance: a theoretical framework. – 3.4. Integrated SCM strategies. – 3.5. The case of ESTAV logistical platform. – 3.6. Triggering innovation in logistics at Villandrea Local Health Authority: where to start?

3.1. Definition of supply chain management in healthcare

As explained in chapter one, OM in the healthcare sector has to do with the optimization of two different types of flows: (i) patients and (ii) materials. In this latter case, we need to refer to the paradigm of Supply chain management (SCM), a relatively new concept that promotes the integration of activities such as the procurement, logistics, production and distribution of products to clients (Stadler, 2008, Zanjirani et al., 2009). Importantly, it also includes coordination and collaboration with channel partners, which can be suppliers, intermediaries, third-party service providers, and customers.

In this sense, supply chain is a broader concept that includes the logistical activities connected with the management of material flows within the company throughout the entire production cycle.

As synthetized in Figure 1, in the case of healthcare organizations, the SCM includes six main phases:

1. Demand Planning.
2. Purchasing & ordering.
3. Warehouse Management[1].
4. Request and validation.
5. Transportation.
6. Administration at production units.

As you can see in the Figure, healthcare SC processes tend to finish with the consignment of the supplies to the production units, since typically the

---

[1] The management of warehouses can be arranged according to two different models: (i) stock and (ii) transit. In the case of the "stock" model supplies arrive, first, at the central WH and are, then, moved towards the different floors while, in the case of the "transit" model, suppliers bring stuff directly to the wards.

client (the patient) arrives to the production site (either an operating room or an ambulatory centre or an Emergency Department) to receive the service. Differently, in the manufacturing sector (e.g., automotive or computer) the management of channels' distribution is very much critical. Only lately, with the growing importance of home care, healthcare delivery organizations have also been required to bring stuff outside the walls of the production units, and this implies a whole set of new challenges.

For many years, manufacturing companies have been aware of the strategic importance of the integration of the different activities across the whole SCM cycle (Ganeshan and Harrison, 1995, Chopra and Meindel, 2007, Stadler, 2008). Recently, the concept of SCM has also gained momentum in the field of healthcare as a tool for increasing productivity and improving quality (Jarret, 1998, Radnor et al., 2006, Doerner and Reiman, 2007).

In the very last years, healthcare delivery organizations have been involved in a series of innovative projects that address two key supply chain (SC) processes: (i) purchasing and (ii) logistics. Both of these processes are economically significant and are considered to be of paramount importance to the improvement of healthcare organization performance.

Figure 1. The main phases of the SCM process.

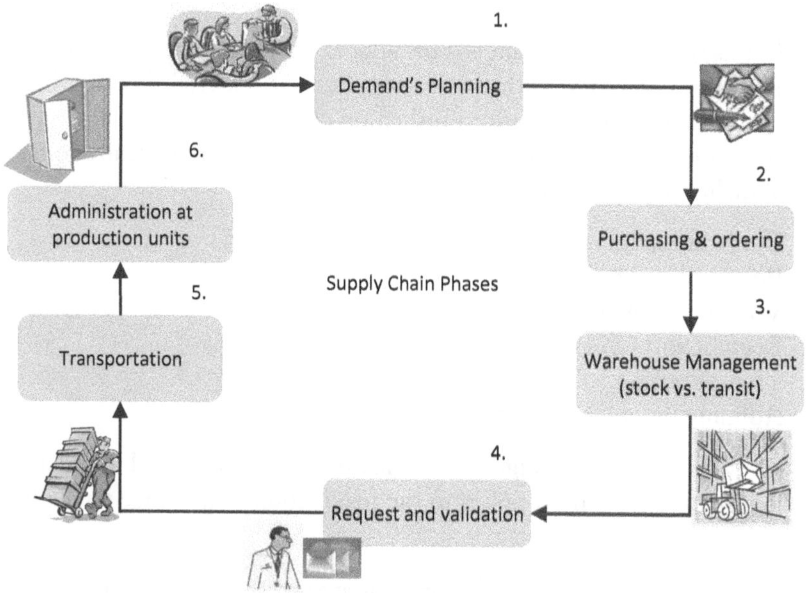

Source: author's elaboration.

In the case of healthcare, there are four different categories of items that go through this cycle, namely:

1. Pharmaceuticals.
2. Medical devices (e.g., stents, valves or orthopaedic prothesis).
3. Healthcare materials.
4. Office and other supplies.

Besides physical goods, there is a critical flow of data that cuts across the different phases of the SC cycle including information about:

- Delivery location.
- Items ordered.
- Inventory levels.
- Quantities and prices paid.
- Location of products in the chain.
- Clinical patient information (patient records, treatment plans, pharmaceutical therapy, etc.).

The ability of providing timely, valid, and accurate flow of information is becoming a distinctive and strategic feature of a modern healthcare supply chain system.

3.2. Innovation trends

The innovations in healthcare SC can be classified along the four logistical framework presented in Paragraph 1.8.

As illustrated in the Figure below the redesign of a SCM system implies the coordinated intervention on four different aspects.

First, it is necessary to make important decisions about the **planning of materials** and the rhythm of the replenishment process for both the central WH and the floors. These choices will have a significant impact on the size of warehouses and on the design of the whole activities that, under some circumstances, can also be successfully delegated to external parties.

Since the bottom line of a supply chain is moving goods around, an important innovation driver is represented by the **physical configuration of the hospital**.

Another important driver is **process reengineering** of the overall SCM cycle with either micro interventions (adopting, for example, the lean approach) or macro changes with hard interventions such as the centralization or the outsourcing of specific phases (for example, the warehouse management).

Finally, in the year 2020, supply chain specialists can rely upon a series of **technological innovations** to help smoothing supplies throughout the different phases of the process, such as:

- Computer Physicians Order Entry (CPOE) system that allows electronic prescription of medicines preventing errors (e.g., over or under dosage) and guaranteeing full traceability of consumption at patient level.
- Radio Frequency Identification (RFiD) used to support inventory management, increase the traceability of supplies, ensure data visibility, and facilitate drugs administration and inventory.
- Automatic Guided Vehicles (AGV) or pneumatic systems for supporting transportation automation.
- Unit dose system to realize the personalized drugs distribution directly at patient's bed.
- Integrated SCM information systems (e.g. Electronic Data Interchange) that provide data and information for analysis, forecasting, management decisions and performance management.
- Smart closets at the floor integrated with central warehouses to store drugs, medical devices, and healthcare materials to avoid waste and to guarantee real-time and up-date information on the level of stocks.

Figure 2. The logistical drivers for SC innovation.

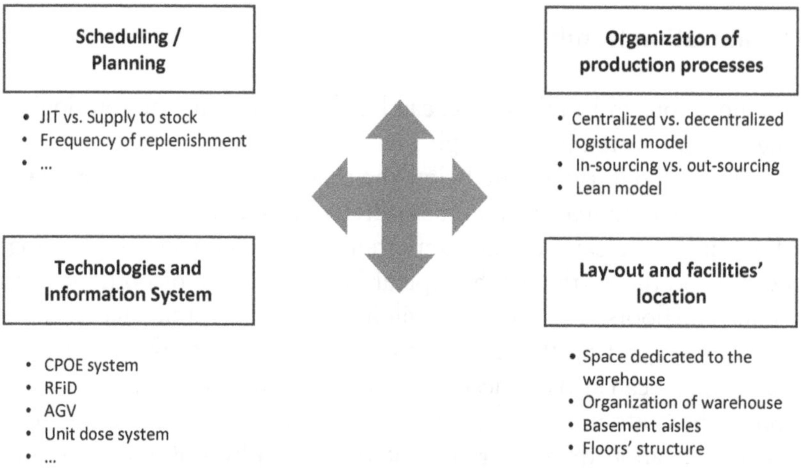

Scheduling / Planning	Organization of production processes
• JIT vs. Supply to stock • Frequency of replenishment • ...	• Centralized vs. decentralized logistical model • In-sourcing vs. out-sourcing • Lean model
Technologies and Information System	**Lay-out and facilities' location**
• CPOE system • RFiD • AGV • Unit dose system • ...	• Space dedicated to the warehouse • Organization of warehouse • Basement aisles • Floors' structure

Source: adapted from Bowersox DJ, Closs DJ (1996) Logistical management: the integrated supply chain. McGraw Hill.

If we look at the scheduling decisions, there are, basically, two main different models:

1. <u>Just in Time</u>: a stockless environment where materials and resources are received when they are needed for consumption.
2. <u>Supply to stock (STS)</u>: Large quantities of materials are purchased and placed into an inventory location for storage and distribution. Typically, items are purchased in bulk quantities to take advantage of pricing discounts and economies of scale; the items are then broken down into smaller units of measure for internal storage.

Both models have pros and cons; it is, furthermore, important to stress the fact that there is not a one-fits-all model, but it depends on the specific characteristics of each single item. A quite common classification of supplies is the so-called ABC classification that classify materials based on the unitary cost and the frequency of use, in particularly:

"A" products: high dollar and low frequency;
"B" products: moderate dollars and items;
"C" products: low dollar, high volume.

As illustrated in figure 3, typically for "A" type products (high unitary cost and low frequency) the most fitting model is the JIT. In the case of healthcare sector products, such as cardiac valves, stents or orthopedic prosthesis, fall in this category. We are talking about quite delicate products where a possible situation of stock-out would have serious consequences for the health of the patients; in this sense, a JIT model would imply high levels of risks. Furthermore, in some cases, demand for a specific product (think for example to cardiac valves) is created only when surgeons "open up" patients during surgeries. In this very peculiar scenario, hospitals are moving towards a modified version of the JIT model so called "Consignment Stock" where all the products are physically located within the hospital, but they are paid to the supplier only when they are used on the patient (e.g., implantation of an orthopedic prosthesis).

In the case of costly products with a frequent use, some hospitals have also demanded to the suppliers the responsibility to manage inventories with their own personnel within the hospital.

Finally, in the case of type "C" products (high use and low unitary cost) a typical fitting scheduling system is the STS model.

However, the ABC classification does not consider the physical space needed to store the supply in the warehouse. Therefore, in the case of "C" products that occupy large spaces (a typical example is the infusion liquid) some hospitals have adopted the so-called Vendors' Management Inventory (VMI) that implies that providers are responsible for both the management of inventories (at their site) and for the weekly replenishment of the floors. In this case, hospitals can rely upon significant discounts thanks to bulk purchases and, at the same time, do not waste space to store bulky items.

Paragraph 3.4 provides a focus on this type of partnerships with suppliers summarizing the most relevant evidence of a study about the benefits and the organizational conditions to successfully implement this type of partnership strategies.

Figure 3. ABC classification for scheduling strategies.

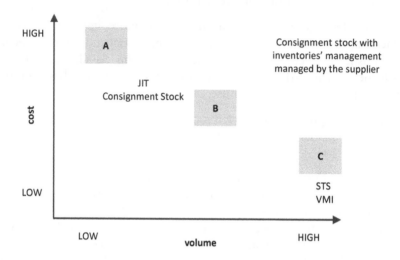

Source: author's elaboration.

Organization of SC processes

In the design of all SCM process, two aspects have become, in the last few years, very relevant:

1. The centralization of warehouses;
2. The outsourcing of key SC activities to external providers.

As for the first aspect, the organization of WHs can follow different models:

1. Warehouses located at each single production unit with the possibility of adoption of the so-called smart closets which guarantee complete traceability of items' flows.
2. Decentralized warehouses: the traditional model to organize supplies implies the creation of two separate spaces one dedicated to drugs and medical devices managed by pharmacists and another one for office supplies and other goods.

3. Hospital WH where all type of supplies is stored and, then, sent, upon request, to all different production units.
4. Outsourcing of the WH activities to an external provider that can be either a private external company or a new inter-hospitals entity created just for this purpose[2].

Figure 4. Different organizational models for the management of warehouses.

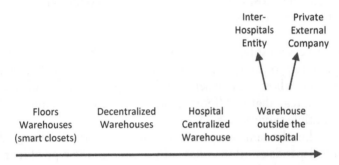

Source: author's elaboration.

As for the second aspect, we are assisting worldwide to successful experiences of outsourcing strategies of different types of activity such as:

- Replenishment of OR block.
- Transportation.
- Warehouse management.
- Drugs re-packaging.
- Sterilization.
- Stocks' management at floors.
- ...

The scientific literature identifies two main conditions that are essential to make these outsourcing projects work:

1. A good understanding of the process being outsourced.
2. Establishing clear and measurable service-level expectations and performance requirements for suppliers and systematically monitoring them.

There are, on the other hand, three main categories of risks associated to these types of partnership:

---

[2] The Chapter 3.5 describes the case of ESTAV that represents a significant and successful example of centralization of the activities of purchasing and logistics through the creation of an inter-hospitals organization that serves seventeen different hospital facilities.

1. Reliability and quality of the supplier.
2. Conflict of interests especially in the case where the logistical services are provided by the same suppliers of other goods (e.g., medicines or medical devices).
3. Heavy reliance on the suppliers on a key strategic process.

Paragraph 3.2 illustrates the main findings of a study conducted by the author about the pros, cons, and organizational conditions for the implementation of partnerships with suppliers.

In any case it must be stressed that any type of SCM innovation strategy must be tailored to the specific characteristics of each single hospital. For example, a niche hospital that serves only a targeted number of service lines requires a strategy that is different from an acute care community hospital treating multiple service lines.

Even within the same hospital structure, a one-fits-all strategy does not exist but it depends on (i) the phase of process, (ii) the type of item considered and (iii) the production unit (see Figure 5).

Figure 5. Logistics hybrid solutions for hospitals.

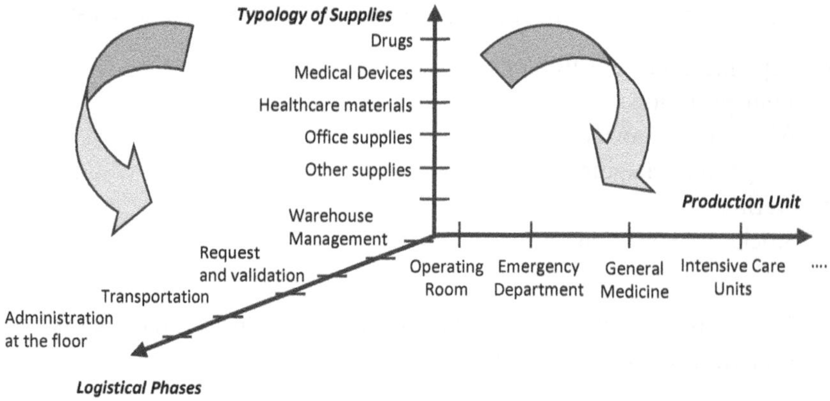

Source: author's elaboration.

3.3. Measuring supply chain performance: a theoretical framework

From a theoretical perspective, a SC system achieves its goals and creates value when it guarantees the purchase of the correct product at a reasonable price allowing the delivery of the correct product in the right condition to the correct location at the correct time, thus ensuring that the expected level of service is provided at the lowest possible cost (Doerner and Reiman, 2007).

Very recently, some studies have attempted to operationalize this concept by proposing different possible performance indicators. The supply chain reference model (SCOR) developed by the Supply Chain Council is the most often quoted in the scientific literature and provides a useful framework for assessing the SC performance of any type of organization. The SCOR model identifies five measurement criteria for assessing the performance of a SC: (1) reliability, (2) responsiveness, (3) flexibility, (4) costs, and (5) efficiency in managing assets (Zanijrani et al., 2009). Within these five broad categories, the Supply Chain Council has promoted the use of 13 performance metrics.

Another possibility is to measure SC performance using the popular and consolidated Balanced Scorecard framework (Kaplan and Norton, 1992) that includes four broad dimensions: (i) customer satisfaction, (ii) internal processes, (iii) company financial performance, and (iv) individual employees.

With the colleagues Lega and Marsilio (Lega et al., 2013) we have developed a theoretical framework for measuring SC performance that takes into account the specificities of public healthcare delivery organizations (cfr. Par. 1.2).

Particularly, the model includes three broad dimensions, as illustrated in Figure 6:

(1) Set-up and operating costs.
(2) Financial benefits.
(3) Organizational and process benefits.

Figure 6. Performance dimensions of healthcare supply chain.

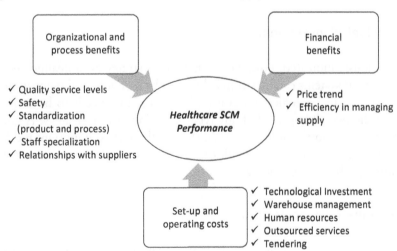

Sources: Lega, Marsilio and Villa (2013).

This framework reduces the number of evaluation dimensions compared to that included in the SCOR model, but adds some performance indicators that have more relevance to the healthcare sector (e.g., 'safety' in the organizational benefits category and 'supply prices' as a financial benefit).

In the following paragraph, we provide a definition of each performance dimension and a short guide on how to calculate the most relevant indicators included in the model.

Set-Up and operating costs

As indicated by the SCOR model, developing and managing a SC system entails a series of set-up and operating costs. There are few studies that propose a framework for measuring management costs in a healthcare SC system. One of the most quoted is the work of Norris (1988), which identifies seven different types of costs related to each SC process, from the cost of the items purchased (including direct costs and transaction costs) to the related utilization costs.

In the study conducted with the colleagues Marsilio and Lega (Lega and Marsilio, 2013), instead, we have classified costs according to different possible cost drivers namely: (i) technology infrastructure, (ii) human resources, (iii) warehouse management costs, (iii) outsourced services, and (iv) advertisement tendering costs (i.e., the way in which public organizations acquire products). Thus, for example, the price of the items purchased is not considered a cost in this system; instead, it is considered an output of the SC process and it is a variable included among the financial benefits. Below there is a brief description of each cost driver.

Technological investment

As previously indicated, nowadays, innovations strategies in healthcare SC management systems can be strongly boosted by technological innovation.

However, technological innovation has a cost that needs to be considered in the overall appraisal of any type of SC innovation strategy. A good cost proxy is amortization rates, even though there is an important hidden cost linked to the training activities for healthcare professionals to get acquainted to the new technology.

Warehouse management costs

Efficient warehouse management is an essential precondition of optimizing SCM (Poulin, 2003, Baker, 2006; Lega et al., 2013).

The performance of warehouse management is usually measured using operating productivity indicators that are typically expressed in units (e.g., lines, orders, cases, pieces, pallets, and pounds).

In these analyses, it is important to also consider costs related to warehouse management, including the cost of space, capital investment and workload (Hackman et al., 2001). A good proxy for capital cost is the amortization rate, whereas in determining the cost of space, it is possible to use rental costs or opportunity cost (the latter if the organization owns the property in question). Workload can be measured in terms of the number of lines shipped, the number of requests cleared or, more approximately, the human resource involved in warehouse activities.

Finally, it is important to consider running costs related to warehouse management, including the cost of utility, cleaning, and security services.

Human resources dedicated to purchasing and logistics activities

In healthcare delivery organizations, the labor workforce accounts for approximately 60% of hospital costs (Poulin, 2003). Therefore, in SC, one of the most relevant cost drivers is the time invested by personnel (staff involved, at different levels, in the management of activities such as procurement, logistical, accounting, and financial staff) in SC processes.

Full Time Equivalents (FTEs) are the most common measures used. It must be noted that in the public sector, a reduction in FTEs resulting from an increase in process efficiency seldom causes a dismissal. More frequently, a reduction in overlapping work can result in FTE staff being reallocated to higher value-added activities or to retired staff not being replaced.

Costs of outsourced services

As reported in several studies (Jarret, 1998, Aptel and Pourjalali, 2001, Nicholson et al., 2004, Moschuri and Kondyilis, 2006), many SC activities, including transportation, warehouse management and drug re-packaging, can be effectively externalized. Even if it has been proved that these outsourcing strategies allow important performance improvements in terms of cost and quality, these benefits need to be balanced with the payments made to external companies for services rendered.

As shown by a very recent study conducted with the colleagues Belvedere and Laratro (Belvedere et al., 2020) lately suppliers (e.g., pharmaceutical or medical devices companies) have been including in their contracts also logistical services such as JIT (Just in Time) or VMI (Vendor Management Inventories). In such a way, we are witnessing to a shift of relationship from client-buyer to partners. The following paragraph illustrates more in-depth these solutions analyzing pros, cons, and organizational conditions to implement this type of partnerships.

Advertisement tendering cost

As illustrated in Paragraph 1.4, OM strategies are constrained by a series of specificities that characterize public institutions.

The need to achieve important public values such as transparency, legality and equity (Lega et al., 2013) makes the procurement process particularly cumbersome and time consuming.

For example, EU Directives set special requirements on the public procurement tendering process, requiring the advertisement of tenders in specific national journals and/or in the Official Journal of the European Community and the TED database (Gelderman et al., 2006).

Financial benefits

A well-performing public healthcare SC is expected to guarantee two different important financial benefits:

(1) reductions in purchasing prices and
(2) reductions in the volume of supplies stocked internally (either those stocked at central warehouses or those stocked at medical department warehouses).

Price trends
Price trends for goods and services can be used to compare the performance of different procurement strategies, especially in public contests in which resources are scarce and the number of purchases is extraordinarily large[3]. Thus, even a small percentage reduction in price can translate into millions of euros in savings (Nollet et al., 2008).

The recent wave of centralizations of the purchasing process, occurred at national and international level, is aimed at achieving significant price reductions through economies of scale obtained by pooling volumes of standardized products.

---

[3] Under a methodological perspective, in these analyses of price benchmarking, it is important to compare homogeneous categories of products and services, alternatively the risk is to arrive to misleading conclusions.

Chapter 3.4 analyzes the impact, on several dimensions, of the creation of a centralized SC platform in Tuscany region.

Efficiency in managing supplies.
For healthcare organizations, supply optimization represents an important area for improvement (Holmgren and Wentz, 1982; Jarret, 1998; Lega et al., 2013). One of the key dimensions of SC performance is the ability to optimize the flow of supplies through the production cycle to minimize the amount of stock at the central warehouse and at medical department warehouses. Possible indicators used to reflect this characteristic of an organization are (Chase et al., 2004):

- the value of warehouse stock;
- the value of stock in hospital wards;
- the value of expired supplies.

Other (non-monetary) indicators are:

- turnover rate: the ratio of the value of goods delivered in a year to the average amount of stock available in the warehouse.
- covering rate (expressed in number of days) is the time period when production demand can be met using the average amount of supplies available at the warehouse and it is calculated as follows: average amount stocked/daily consumption.

In the healthcare sector, traditional manufacturing performance indicators must be used with caution. At least two factors need to be considered:

(i) the cost of supply stock-outs is high because patient health is at stake; in other words, the cost of the shortage of life-saving medicine is the same life of the patient being treated.
(ii) healthcare production processes are subject to a certain degree of natural variability (see Paragraph 1.5), which is difficult and costly to handle when inventory levels are low.

There is a certain trade-off between keeping stocks at a minimum level and the ability to respond in a timely and effective way to the natural fluctuations of the demand.

This trade-off can be graphically represented by the boat in Figure 7: you do not want to hit the peaks of the coast but, on the other end, keeping such a high minimum stock level is costly; ideally you want to move to scenario "b" where the coast (in our metaphor the demand for care) is less rugged and steep.

To achieve this goal, there are two different strategies:

1. reducing variability in the demand through a better scheduling system (see Par 2.1).
2. reducing the variety of products references.

In this latter case, the way to achieve this goal is to work with end users (e.g., doctors, nurses, or administrative staff) to verify the actual necessity of a variety of different references for the same product. A simple example might clarify this concept: do we really need ten different pens' colors or black and red are sufficient?

Figure 7. Trade-off between stocks' levels and capability of meeting the demand.

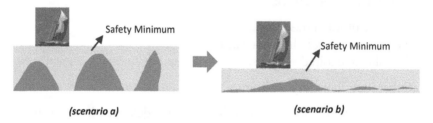

(scenario a)   *(scenario b)*

Source: author's elaboration.

Organizational and process benefits

A high-performing healthcare supply chain is expected to guarantee several different important organizational and process benefits related to:

(1) Product and process standardization.
(2) Staff specialization and workload optimization.
(3) Quality service levels.
(4) Safety, and
(5) Supplier relationships.

Standardization
As seen in Paragraph 1.2 managing healthcare production processes is more challenging due to the presence of different sources of variability.

For this reason, standardization represents a critical success factor when a healthcare organization is seeking to promote the adoption of an innovative SC approach and is, therefore, relevant to the design and management of any type of healthcare OM system (McKone-Sweet et al., 2005).

As outlined earlier, to optimize the management of stocks, it is important to reduce variability in the demand of care and the variety of items used (cfr. the example of pens' colors).

We stress also, the fact there is room to standardize the overall SCM process. Some examples in this sense are:

(i) the percentage of requests that are urgent;
(ii) the ratio of the number of emergency orders to the number of units of products stocked;
(iii) the duration of the procurement process;
(iv) the frequency of materials' transportation to the floors;
(v) the presence of a common list of products used throughout the organization.

Staff specialization and workload optimization.
Under this dimension, we include two different aspects.

First, as already said, healthcare delivery organizations manage a complex variety of supplies that require different skills, knowledge and organizational models. However, the purchasing and logistical departments of healthcare organizations are typically functional units staffed by generalists who lack specific education and training considered critical for successful SC implementation (Gowen III and Tallon 2003, Callendar and McGuire 2007). It is, thus, important to create specialized units focusing on the purchasing of specific categories of products for example drugs or medical devices.

In the case of ESTAV (see Chapter 3.5) the centralization of the platform represented an important driver in the redesign of the whole organizational model with the creation of units dedicated to all SCM process for particular items.

A second aspect is linked to the fact that, within healthcare SCM systems, still pharmacist and nurses perform a significant part of logistical activities.

An interesting study (Hendrich et al. 2008), using radio-frequency identification tags (RFID), shows, for example, that only 20% of nursing time is spent on direct patient-care activities with direct negative consequences on clinical outcome such as higher rates of mortality and readmissions.

The same is true for pharmacists who are too often employed in logistical activities instead of being put in the condition of playing a much more valuable role in supporting doctors in clinical governance activities.

It is, thus, very much important to redesign SCM processes to save precious time for nurses and pharmacists.

Quality of service
The concept of quality in the case of SCM can be spelled out in different ways but several authors (Riopel et al. 2005, Mazzocato 2007, Zanijrani et al. 2009, Bensa et al. 2010, Lega et al. 2013) identify three main dimensions:

(1) reliability;

(2) responsiveness;

(3) flexibility.

We propose, here, four main indicators that we consider more valid and accurate to measure the overall quality of a healthcare SC system:

(1) Time to deliver.

The time needed to move a particular inventory item from its point of storage to the end user.

(2) Accuracy of information.

It has to do with the information about movement of goods within an organization. A proxy to measure this dimension is any misalignment between what is reported 'on the books' and actual inventory levels.

(3) Lead time.

Time from the order to the supplier and the physical arrival of the good to the hospital.

(4) Reliability.

Number of cases of stock-out in a year.

Safety

Safety is a crucial factor in healthcare logistics because even the smallest mistake can have major consequences for patient health. In relation to drug logistics, several studies suggest that error rates during each step in drug management (prescription, transcription of prescriptions, delivery and administration) vary between 14% (Tissot et al., 2003) and 43% (Lisby et al., 2005). So far, very few studies have attempted to determine the effect of different logistical models on patient safety (Taxis et al., 1999, Fontain et al., 2003), however, it is critical to include clinical risk management indicators in the overall appraisal of a healthcare SC system.

Supplier relationship management

The importance of supplier relationship management has been widely recognized in the literature (Cox et al., 2005b). SC innovation can offer opportunities to improve supplier management along various dimensions and especially through the adoption of selection criteria for quality/price benchmarking and strategic network supply management (Lamming et al., 2000, Petroni and Braglia, 2000).

Compared to other industries the healthcare sector, partly because of the public nature of many organizations, has lagged in developing partnerships with suppliers. However, as shown by a recent study conducted with the colleagues Belvedere and Laratro, lately healthcare organizations have started to build successful partnerships with suppliers on a variety of different areas.

The next Paragraph will provide some highlights of the main findings of this study.

3.4. Integrated SCM strategies

As anticipated in the previous Paragraph, in the very last years, even in the healthcare sector, the idea of logistics has been replaced by the broader concept of Supply Chain Management (SCM).

SCM represents *"the integration of business processes from end user through original suppliers that provides products, service and information that add value for customers"* (Cooper et al., 1997).

Unlike logistics, SCM implies a more comprehensive approach that aims to create a network of organizations that are involved, through upstream and downstream linkages, in the different processes and activities that produce value in the form of products and services delivered to the ultimate consumer (Christopher, 1992).

The Supply Chain Integration in the healthcare field, specifically related to the hospital-supplier partnership, was defined by Chen et al. (2013) as *"the extent to which the business processes between a hospital and its key suppliers are strategically coupled and unified as a whole"*.

These types of strategies, however, are still far from common in healthcare, although the use of SCM is expanding rapidly between healthcare provider (Bensa et al., 2010), a trend explained by the pressure of performance improvement in the healthcare services linked to the limited resources and to the need to achieve more value (Lega et al., 2013).

The integration between healthcare delivery organizations and suppliers is also fostered by the flow of products' innovation, think for example to the use of 3D printing in the production of orthopedic prosthesis or the genetic therapy for the care of oncological problems.

In the latter case a very fitting example is the CAR T-cell therapy, a type of treatment in which patient's T cells (a type of immune system cell) are treated in the laboratories of pharmaceutical companies and then infused to the patient at the hospital to kill cancer cells[4].

Literature review (Belevedere et al., 2019) outlines that, for healthcare delivery organizations, such collaborative partnerships are beneficial for several reasons such as: (i) higher levels of reliability of replenishments; (ii)

---

[4] CAR T-cell therapy is used to treat certain blood cancers but, recently, it is being studied in the treatment of other types of cancer.

timeliness; (iii) flexibility; (iv) safety; (v) workload reduction for hospital staff and (vi) efficiency in managing supplies (namely covering rate and rotation index).

In a recent study conducted with the colleagues Belvedere and Laratro (Belvedere et al., 2019) we have analyzed the status of the current practices of SCM strategies adopted by healthcare organizations in the region of center north of Italy.

Particularly the research represents the level of diffusion of integration between healthcare delivery organizations and providers with particular attention to the following collaborative practices:

Just in Time (JIT)

As already mentioned in the previous paragraph, materials scheduling and replenishment can be designed according two different opposite models (i) JIT (Just In Time) versus (i) STS (Supply To Stock). In this latter case, large quantities of materials are purchased and placed at the central warehouse for storage and distribution. Typically, items are purchased in bulk quantities to take advantage of pricing discounts and economies of scale. On the contrary, the JIT model implies a stockless environment where materials and resources are received when they are needed for consumption. This requires a much stronger involvement by suppliers and daily replenishments.

RFID system

RFID is an acronym for "radio-frequency identification" and refers to a technology whereby digital data encoded in RFID tags or smart labels are captured by a reader via radio waves. RFID is similar to barcoding in that data from a tag or label are captured by a device that stores the data in a database. RFID, however, has several advantages over systems that use barcode asset tracking software. The most notable is that RFID tag data can be read outside the line-of-sight, whereas barcodes must be aligned with an optical scanner. The prerequisite of the implementation of this type of system is that each item is tagged with a RFID code and this implies a strong collaboration with the suppliers. [5]

---

[5] The study "RFID in Healthcare" (Bearing Point and National Alliance for Healthcare Information Technology 2006) found that RFID technology is being used in a variety of applications within the healthcare industry, including patient flow logistics, access control and security, supply chain systems and smart shelving. Real time medical equipment tracking systems and patient safety systems, such as those for identification and medication administration, were found to be the major areas where RFID is expected to be used in the future (McLaughlin and Hays, 2008).

Electronic Data Interchange (EDI)

EDI provides a direct electronic link between a manufacturer's database and that of its vendors.

This evidently implies a strong partnership between suppliers and heath care providers that pass through the adoption of similar software and of a common informatics language.

In general, a customer typically establishes an EDI link only with a few vendors. In this scenario, potential new vendors have to demonstrate significant improvements in price and/or quality to warrant the additional costs of an added EDI link.

Vendor Management Inventories (VMI)

We refer to a situation in which a supplier of goods, usually the manufacturer, is responsible for managing the inventory on behalf of the final client, in our case the healthcare delivery organizations. This model can prevent the stocking of undesired inventories and hence can lead to an overall cost reduction. This SCM strategy is typically suggested for low cost-high volume items (see the ABC matrix illustrated in the previous chapter) and for voluminous supplies, that consume uselessly valuable space at the hospital floors, such as infusion liquids or material for dialysis.

This approach is, sometimes, referred to as the "bread man method". The term "bread man" comes from commercial bakeries, where the bread man (or salesmen) determines the number of loaves of bread to deliver to each retail outlet on their routes and is also responsible for placing the bread on the retailers' shelves.

With this approach, minimum and maximum inventory levels are established for each item. The firm's suppliers are then empowered to determine how often these items should be replenished. In addition, the suppliers have direct access to the manufacturing floors and usually restock the items at the points where they will be used. This eliminates the need for stockrooms. With this approach, paperwork is reduced significantly because no purchase orders are generated. The receiving function is also significantly reduced, as is the need for personnel to move the items from the stockroom onto the manufacturing floor.

Proactive management of expired goods

Product life cycles continue to shorten as competition introduces new products at an ever-increasing rate in the hope of gaining market share and a competitive advantage. To respond quickly to the introduction of new products, a company needs to have flexible processes that can be converted easily to new product requirements. Flexibility can also be achieved by shifting more responsibility onto suppliers (Davis and Heineke, 2005). In the case of healthcare, specific items, such as medicines or medical de-

vices, require specific attention in the management of supply chain cycle regarding stock's conditions (e.g., temperature) or expiration date.

Collaborative planning and forecasting

When each supply chain member develops its forecast based only on the orders of its immediate customer, then higher order fluctuations are typically observed and one moves up the supply chain. For instance, retailers may exaggerate their forecasts to protect against unforeseen surges in demand. Distributors, having observed only the retailers' orders (and not the actual end consumer demand), may exaggerate orders even more (Davis and Heineke, 2005). In the case of healthcare, collaborative scheduling has great potentials, but it requires high levels of IT integration between supplier and healthcare organizations in order to achieve full traceability of the entire process, at least, at three critical points: (i) suppliers' warehouse; (ii) hospital central warehouse and (iii) production units. This integration is enhanced with the physical presence of the supplier at the hospital through the adoption of organizational models such as the consignment stock (see below).

Consignment Stock

In recent years there has been increased emphasis on the management of a firm's assets, as measured by the rate of return on assets, and the bonuses of many managers are directly related to this measure. Inasmuch as inventories are viewed as an asset on a firm's balance sheet, the less inventory that is on hand, the better the return on assets. To reduce inventories without negatively affecting operations and customer deliveries, an increasing number of companies are using **consignment inventories** *wherever possible. Consignment inventories are inventories that are physically in a company's facility but are still owned by the supplier. Thus, they do not appear anywhere as an asset to the firm. Only when the components are actually used in the production the supplier charges the buyer. Consignment inventories are also used in services, where the retailer does not pay the manufacturer for the product until is sold to the end user (Davis and Heineke, 2015). This model is extensively used in healthcare for "A" type products (see Figure 3.3): low use and high unitary cost. This model is particularly appropriate for healthcare where, in some occasions, you don't know the exact product you need in the production process until the very end; for example, the exact size of a cardiac valve is known only when the surgeon opens up the patient's chest. A possible evolution of the consignment stock model is the presence of suppliers' employees, directly at the production unit (e.g., operating room), in charge of all logistical activities (see below).*

Warehouse managed by the supplier.

This situation can be seen as an evolution of both JIT and consignment stock models; in fact, in some cases, academics and professionals refer to this model as JIT 2.0 (Davis and Heineke, 2005).

In any case the objective is for the vendor and customer to work much closer together, thereby eliminating many of the intermediate steps that now exist. To accomplish this, a vendor employee is provided with physical office space within the purchasing function of the customer. This approach eliminates the need for a buyer for the customer and a salesperson for the vendor.

This vendor representative has full access to the customer's database and therefore can translate the customer's purchase orders directly into orders for his or her company. This individual also participates in the customer's new-product design process, offering suggestions for improving product performance and/or reducing costs. The three elements for successfully implementing this model are (i) the physical presence of the vendor's representative inside the customer's manufacturing facility and, at the same time, (ii) the ability to provide the direct data linkage between the customer's planning function and the vendor's manufacturing facility (iii) the reliability of the supplier in terms of trust, competences, and technological standards (Davis and Heineke, 2015).

Together with the colleagues Belvedere and Laratro (Belvedere et al. 2019) we have conducted a survey to understand the current state of implementation of these collaborative practices adopted by healthcare delivery organizations[6] in the regions of center-north of Italy.

The survey has been filled out by 67 organizations reaching an overall response rate of 50%; the table below summarizes some key findings of the study.

Table 1. Examples of collaborative SCM projects.

Integration practice	Projects	
	a. v.	%
Just in Time	51	20%
Collaborative planning and forecasting	43	16%
Consignment stock	41	16%
EDI	33	13%
Proactive management of expired items	31	12%
Vendor Management Inventory	23	9%
Warehouse managed by the supplier	23	9%
RFiD	13	5%
Others	3	1%
Total	261	100%

Source: adapted from Belvedere et al., 2019.

---

[6] Particularly, we have included in the study public Local Health Authorities, public independent Trusts and private accredited hospitals with more that 400 beds.

The study shows that half of these collaborative projects have been focusing on two categories of items: (i) medical devices and (ii) materials used in the operating rooms.

Organizational conditions

While academics and professionals all agree that, in the near future, collaborations between suppliers and providers will be very much critical still few studies have analyzed the conditions to make these collaborative strategies actually work.

Summarizing the main contributions in this area (Power, 2005; Crook et al., 2007; Fawcett et al., 2008; Villa, 2012) we can, at least, identify eight enabling conditions:

(i)   ICT logistical platform capable of providing accurate information at the right place, at the right time, and in the right hands;
(ii)   process standardization;
(iii)   strong commitment of top management;
(iv)   strategic relevance of logistics;
(v)   clear goals of improvement;
(vi)   skilled employees across department and organizational functions;
(vii)   bargaining power from the providers;
(viii) control system of Supply chain performance.

Furthermore, as outlined throughout chapter one, in the analysis of SCM strategies, it is important to take into account the specificities of healthcare production processes and the public nature of most of healthcare delivery organizations.

The study conducted with the colleagues Belvedere and Laratro (Belvedere et al., 2019) highlights the relevance of some organizational factors, such as the strategic relevance of the Logistic function as well as the commitment of the top management for the success of an integration process.

Furthermore, standardization (either process or product standardization) in not considered a positive consequence of this integration strategies but, on the contrary, an essential condition for successfully implementing these projects.

This confirms the necessity – outlined by an extensive body of literature (Vissers, 1998, Haraden and Resar, 2004, Litvak et al., 2005, Walley and Steyn, 2006, Villa et al., 2014) – to eliminate, within the healthcare delivery organizations, the so called artificial variability through organizational strategies such as better scheduling and capacity management systems or the introduction of clinical pathways to standardize the clinical decision making process. Reductions in products' variety and higher levels of process standardization should allow relevant improvements along the whole healthcare supply chain.

As outlined by McLaughlin and Hays, an important prerequisite of standardization strategies is process analysis, including a thorough and complete understanding of existing systems, process and protocols (through process mapping) (McLaughlin and Hays, 2008).

Finally, concerning barriers to implementation, the cost of the technology and, in particular, the integration of IT systems with the suppliers seem to be critical issues to be addressed.

The study conducted with the colleagues Belvedere and Laratro concludes with a series of significant case studies. As already mentioned, the most popular type of partnership is the consignment stock for medical devices used in operating rooms in specialties such as orthopedics, cardiac surgery and plastic surgery. In this case, the rationale for integration with the suppliers is linked with the necessity of having the widest possible range of items without buying them because, in many cases, the surgeons find out which device (e.g. cardiac valve) they really need only when the surgery is occurring.

This type of model ensures several benefits like (i) no risk of stock-outs, (ii) better management of expiration dates (iii) traceability guaranteed by a dedicated software and (iii) continuous product innovation from the suppliers.

On the contrary, this type of model requires an investment in training for nurses managing products at the operating room block and for administrative people who are required to develop law skills to get by the several constrains imposed by the public law and logistical competences to effectively interact with suppliers.

Finally, successful best practices show that, in order to realize these types of projects, it is of paramount importance the collaboration between all the different offices involved in the supply chain cycle, namely (i) purchasing office; (ii) logistics and operations office; (iii) medical directory and (iv) HTA unit.

In conclusion, we have been witnessing, in the healthcare sector, a trend, common to other sectors, of a shift in the role of the supplier from being purely transactional, based mainly on cost, to being a partner that participates in strategic decisions of the organizations.

As outlined in the scientific literature (Davis and Heineke, 2015), the reasons behind this growing importance of these integration strategies are different: (i) the need of concentrating on core competencies (in the case of healthcare clinical activities); (ii) increased need for flexibility and (iii) a desire to sharing financial risk with the suppliers especially in occasion of the launch of new processes or products.

3.5. The case of ESTAV logistical platform

In this paragraph we briefly describe the case of ESTAV a logistical platform, developed in the center of Tuscany, to serve public healthcare delivery organizations. This case, deeply analyzed with the colleagues Lega and Marsilio (Lega et al., 2013), represents a good setting to test the performance framework illustrated in Figure 6.

ESTAV Centro is a public agency in charge of managing the integration of SC processes for a network of 17 public hospitals with approximately 4,400 beds that serve 1.5 million citizens in the Tuscany region (Italy)[7].

ESTAV is in charge of all procurement processes (from the collection of member requests to the signing of contracts with winning suppliers)[8] and coordinates the overall logistical activities (from the receipt of supplies at a central warehouse to the delivery of requested supplies directly to hospital floors on a daily basis).

The ESTAV model adopted in the Tuscany region was the first launched across the country but it belongs to a established international trend of consolidation of the supply chain function. International examples of such organizations or platforms are the PASA Agency, OCG Buying Solutions and the NHS supply chain in UK, CADES in Switzerland, CACIC and other national and regional initiatives in France, and CHC in Spain (Marsilio and Mele 2010).

With the colleagues Lega and Marsilio (Lega et al., 2013) we have conducted a seven-years longitudinal study to assess the strength of the model presented in Paragraph 3.3 along the three dimensions of (i) operational costs; (ii) organizational benefits and (iii) financial benefits (see Figure 6).

---

[7] Currently, the ESTAV model has been partly replaced by ESTAR, a regional-wide center that is in charge for all purchasing activities for the public healthcare delivery organizations located in the Region.

[8] Very recently, an increasing number of purchasing activities has been taken over by a regional entity called ESTAR.

Table 2. ESTAV: impact on operating costs.

	Dimension	Indicators	Before centralization	With centralization
Operational cost	Warehouse management costs	Number of warehouses	26	1
		Square meters occupied	11.173	9.500
		Running costs	746.840	635.000**
		Renting cost	1.552.487	1.320.000**
	Human resources dedicated to purchasing and logistics	Full Time Equivalents dedicated to logistics activities	263	107
		− Administrative staff dedicated to logistics	108	51
		− Administrative staff dedicated to purchasing	111	52
		− Pharmacists	44	4
		Costs of full time equivalents dedicated to logistics activities	11.176.800	3.918.200
		− Administrative staff dedicated to logistics	3.434.400	1.621.800
		− Administrative staff dedicated to purchasing	4.218.000	1.976.000
		− Pharmacists	3.524.400	320.400
	Costs of outsourced services	Annual cost for the distribution function	n.a.	302.000
	Administrative tendering costs	Costs saving	−	718.170**

** These voice are an average on the 7 ESTAV operating years.

Source: adapted from Lega, Marsilio, Villa (2013).

Table 3. ESTAV: impact on financial benefits.

	Prices trend	% savings/amount awarded	−	5,30%
Financial benefits	Supplies optimization	Warehouse stock value (EURO)	19.803.394	10.874.087
		Turnover rate	7	10
		Covering rate (days)	50	38

** These voice are an average on the 7 ESTAV operating years.

Source: adapted from Lega, Marsilio, Villa (2013).

The tables included above show important numbers.

In terms of **operational costs**, we outline (i) a reduction of - 350,000 EURO (yearly base) of running and renting costs; (ii) a reduction of human resources dedicated to SC activities equal to 156 FTE (Full Time Equivalents) corresponding to a figurative economic value of 7 million of EURO; (iii) the organizational costs linked to all tendering processes decreased by 5 million EURO.

Concerning the reduction of FTE it is important to clarify a key aspect: the reduction of human resources dedicated to purchasing and logistical activities does not bring real savings and, therefore, does not have an impact on hospital financial statements, it is, typically, complicated, especially in public organizations, to dismiss people. However, a reduction in overlapping work can result in FTE staff being reallocated to higher-value added-ed activities or to retired staff not being replaced.

For example the centralization of logistic activity in a single warehouse has been seen as a unique opportunity to relieve hospital pharmacists from operational responsibilities and increase their involvement in clinical activities.

In this sense, the words of one pharmacist explain very well the situation: *"At the beginning we did not like the innovation brought in by ESTAV, we were afraid we would lose power and control over drugs management. Now, freed up by mere logistical activities, we have time to work at the hospital floors close to physicians, who, regarding medicines, have a lot to learn from us"*.

Now pharmacists are involved in a series of valuable activities, such as providing support to physicians in drug prescription activities, supporting the design and updates of the information system, and evaluating whether drugs requests and consumption trends are appropriate.

In terms of **financial benefits,** we saw a relatively small impact on price trends (about minus 5%) and a more significant impact on supply optimization (e.g., covering rate from 50 to 38) with numbers, however, still far distant from the JIT models adopted in other industries (e.g., automotive).

As indicated in the study conducted with the colleagues Lega and Marsilio the improvement in the efficiency levels can be explained by different factors: (i) the adoption of new organizational approaches to streamline the ordering process for clinical departments (e.g. the Kamban model[9]), (ii) the use of industrial criteria to optimize the amount of supplies at central warehouses, (iii) the supply traceability through bar-coding technology, and (iv) the optimization of space.

Finally, as regards organizational benefits, the creation of a centralized platform has facilitated initiatives intended to enhance product and process standardization. Multi-disciplinary teams (including physicians, pharmacists, clinical engineers and administrative staff) have been created to define shared, standard lists of supplies for the several hospitals. This step towards product standardization has triggered a fundamental process of knowledge sharing that has, eventually, allowed improvements in the clinical appropriateness of medical goods consumption. In fact, being part of a

---

[9] For a description of the Kanban model, we refer the reader to Paragraph 4.1.

network offers the opportunity to use 'internal consulting services' to acquire essential knowledge on particular aspects such as technical characteristics of certain products, prices or characteristics of suppliers.

3.6. Triggering innovation in logistics at Villandrea Local Health Authority: where to start?

This paragraph contains a teaching case that allows to go more in depth about the organization of supply chain in healthcare delivery organizations and the possible impact of innovation in this area.

Particularly, it is possible to structure the class discussion along the following three main research questions:

1. Briefly describe logistics at Villandrea LHA, underlining its pros and cons.
2. What are the main critical points in the way Doctor Pietrafranca managed change?
3. Develop a plan to innovate logistics to be presented to the CEO.

Dr. Pietrafranca, Chief Medical Officer at Villandrea Local Health Authority (LHA), sitting alone in her office, was going through the abundant notes she had taken during the first meeting of the focus group on logistics that she herself had put together just months before.

"The bottom line is: the way logistics is run at our Health Authority isn't working and must be changed. Everybody agrees, but the real question is: where to start?"

Everyone has their own opinion; everyone has identified their own priorities and has suggested which changes to implement first.

Nurses maintain that the first thing to do is changing logistics in the wards, since staff are overloaded with way too many time-consuming tasks which bite into the time they can devote to caring for patients.

The Procurement Manager, on the other hand, holds a different view; supported by the Chief Financial Officer, he thinks that the first thing to do is dealing with logistics in the warehouses. In fact, there has been talk of centralizing and outsourcing warehouse management for quite a long time. The latter is a thorny issue, though: on the one hand, the Local Health District (Area Vasta) has been pushing for a single warehouse catering to all the local health authorities under its supervision, while on the other pharmacists, who traditionally hold a strong position inside the health authority, would not be easy to deal with, all the more because they are still attached to the idea that a pharmaceutical warehouse ought to be managed by pharmacists."

After the early excitement, Dr. Pietrafranca started asking herself why she had accepted the Chief Executive's offer to lead the project to change logistics at the health authority. After all, she told herself, there are many others inside the Authority who might have taken care of this delicate matter more effectively.

Villandrea Local Health Authority: the context

Villandrea Local Health Authority caters to a population of 180,000 residents spread over an area of about 265 km2, in a territory mostly hilly and flat. There is one hospital, "Ospedale della Margherita", with 416 beds, and a licensed healthcare facility, with 108 beds.

Villandrea LHA belongs to the Center Health District in the Giardino region. The Center Health District (AVC), which includes four Local Health Authorities and a hospital, has been created in 2003, with the purpose of centralizing the purchase of pharmaceutical as well as general supplies and, at the same time, identifying guidelines for growth shared by all the authorities of the district. Every month the managers from Center Health District meet to discuss issues in the authorities they are leading and to define common strategies and promote continuous improvement. The issues which had started the most heated debates during the last few meetings were those related to the possible innovations in logistics and the need to streamline the flow of goods through the area.

Doctor Dorino, CFO at Villandrea LHA, had become a fixture of the Center Health District meetings, together with his colleague, the Chief Medical Officer, Doctor Pietrafranca.

Villandrea LHA had been working on centralizing and merging the warehouses of the authority, which were located in two different places: the warehouse for pharmaceutical goods (drugs and medical devices) is located inside Margherita hospital, while the warehouse for office supplies and other goods is 25 km away. The project, however, is on hold, as the LHA, before taking any definitive action, is waiting for a final decision from the Health District on the creation of a single warehouse big enough to cater to all its five local authorities.

Regardless of the strategic choice about warehouse location and layout, the awareness that the whole logistics had to be extensively redesigned was widely shared inside Villandrea, as the current system was proving unable to ensure acceptable levels of efficiency and quality.

Logistics at Villandrea works as follows:

- Purchasing and storage: The purchase request (RDA), is generated, usually once a week, by the pharmacy and staff from the OU Purchase of goods and services. In particular, pharmacists are responsible for approving the requests concerning pharmaceutical goods, and forwarding them to the procurement and supply department, which will deal with administration. Inside the warehouse, the LHA staff, once the goods have been received, checks that the goods delivered are consistent with the order placed, then proceeds to input the order in the authority IT system. After that, the goods are stored in the warehouse, which features conventional layout and equipment.

Goods in transit are managed in a similar way: after the accuracy of the order has been checked, warehouse informs the ward concerned and prepares the delivery, which will be carried out by warehouse personnel.

The Procurement department and the Pharmacy manager have both, each on their own, carried out for months an accurate scrutiny of order management. They hold divergent views on the process, a consequence of their disagreement on which managerial choices to make for streamlining the process itself. The OU Procurement is inclined towards deliveries in bulk, whereas pharmacy prefers deliveries in small batches, which allow for a better turnover of the stock in the warehouse.

This debate, which is of course part and parcel in the ordinary life at any given health authority, had stalled at Villandrea because of the utter lack of communication between the managers of the two units involved. Several times both directors have complained to the CFO who, however, had shown little interest in the matter and seemed quite untroubled by the logistics issues at micro-organizational level.

- Requests by wards: the management of supplies for each operative unit is entrusted to a nurse who, twice a week, outlines the needs of pharmaceutical goods as well as general supplies, devoting to this task about 5/6 hours. Expiry dates are checked once a month, and the process requires 3-4 hours. Inventory of ward stocks is normally performed once a year, and requires 35 nurse/hours. All the activities carried out for managing ward stocks are done by hand, with the only exception of orders, which are sent to the warehouse through the IT system.

- Transportation: transport is entrusted in part to in-house staff and in part outsourced to a cooperative. Transport activities involve 10 people: the 5 from the cooperative deal with logistics in the territory catered by the LHA with deliveries from the office and general goods warehouse towards the Margherita hospital, while the 5 in-house staff deliver goods to the wards, both pharmaceutical goods taken from the hospital warehouse and the general goods left by the people from the cooperative at the hospital gate.

- Prescription in wards: for prescribing drugs, doctors fill a form by hand. Nurses check the information on the form and prepare a cart for administering the therapy: they pick the packages from the ward closet, prepare, if necessary, the drug administered with physiological solution, put together the therapy at the patient bed, and they finally administer the therapy. To prepare the cart, nurses need 4 hours per ward every day, while the administration of drugs takes 15 minutes per patient. In fact, in a ward with 30 beds the nursing staff devotes about 11 hours to logistics activities each day. The tracking of the drugs is guaranteed by paper documents, signed and countersigned by personnel at each step of the process.

How to change logistics: The Chief Medical Officer's project

Doctor Pietrafranca's interest in logistics goes back to her previous job as Quality manager at an LHA in a nearby region. Back then, and very much ahead of the times, Doctor Pietrafranca, had dealt with patient's security.

She had understood that, by improving logistics (whose aim is to make sure that the correct good arrives to the correct patient at the correct time in the correct form) significant improvements could be made to the safety guaranteed to patients.

Therefore, she was quite happy to accept the offer by Villandrea's Chief Executive to take charge of a project for triggering innovation in logistics at the LHA.

She thought that could be the opportunity of a lifetime, to eventually put into practice some of the ideas she had been working on for years.

Recently, however, she had more than once told herself not to make her background in medicine and in quality management have the upper hand. She was very much aware that in decisions concerning logistics there are several issues to be taken into account: costs, efficiency, productivity, impact on the organization, economic and financial impact.

This awareness motivated her decision to create a multidisciplinary team, giving representation to all the different perspectives involved in healthcare logistics. Thus, 14 people were included in the team:

(i)   Two pharmacists.
(ii)   The manager of the Procurement office together with an assistant.
(iii) The Pharmacy director with an assistant.
(iv)   Two nurses.
(v)   The Logistics manager.
(vi)   The Chief Financial Officer and an assistant.
(vii) Two doctors: one chosen by the General Surgery Chief Resident, and the other by the General Medicine Chief Resident.
(viii) One doctor from the Health Direction.

Innovating logistics: where to start?

The goal of the team was first to draw up a document outlining the main strategic guidelines for logistics in the LHA, a sort of manifesto for change in logistics.

The document, in the CEO's intention, should have focused on a two-pronged target. Internally, the document should have channeled energies and resources towards specific and detailed projects for change. Externally, the document should have helped to direct and lead the decisional process at the District level, concerning some specific strategic choices in the logistics field.

Doctor Pietrafranca was pinning her hopes on the contribution of ideas and tips that would come from the team; however, she went to the first meeting having in mind three main issues to focus on:

1. Warehouse management.
2. Transport.
3. Drug management.

On the issue of warehouse management, there were three priorities:

1. Creation of a framework for planning requests.
2. Use of a software in the warehouse interfaced with hospital IT systems.
3. Re-engineering logistics flows, possibly employing innovative organizational models such as JIT or Kamban.

On the issue of transportation Doctor Pietrafranca remarked how the time that a supplier spent in delivering office supplies and general goods to Margherita hospital was about thirty minutes. The supplier was confident he could reduce the time once the new highway under construction in the area had been completed, as the new road allowed to cover the distance between warehouse and hospital in just 16 minutes.

As to delivery to wards, Doctor Pietrafranca was wondering whether it might be useful to change the current delivery system, with the general goods left in a dedicated place inside the hospital, with inside staff charged with carrying the goods from that point to the destination, to a new one with staff from the cooperative delivering directly to each ward. For deliveries to wards, the average carrying time inside the hospital was about 10 minutes per ward.

The management of transportation had become more confused and inefficient in the last few years, with little clarity about the allocation of tasks and roles between the cooperative and the internal staff. The Chief Medical Officer, in fact, was considering the possibility to outsource all transport, outside and inside the hospital, of goods as well as people, to a single operator.

Drugs' Management

The unit-dose model
Doctor Pietrafranca had heard about the unit-dose model because the Garofano LHA, part of the Center District as well, had been using that technology for more than 4 years (see chart below).

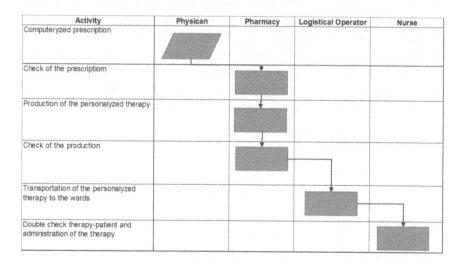

Activity	Physican	Pharmacy	Logistical Operator	Nurse
Computeryzed prescription				
Check of the prescriptiom				
Production of the personalyzed therapy				
Check of the production				
Transportation of the personalyzed therapy to the wards				
Double check therapy-patient and administration of the therapy				

Garofano LHA had always stood out among the authorities belonging to the Center District, for its strong commitment to innovation and for experimenting with new organizational solutions.

Garofano LHA caters to a territory of 4000 km2, where there are two hospitals with 256 and 344 beds respectively. They are located about 87 km away.

The goal of supplying both hospitals with personalized therapies was very bold, but after 4 years it can be safely stated that the unit-dose model has been successful.

Pharmacy, with equipment for the production of personalized therapies, is located in the bigger hospital and transport of therapies is performed every day by an external company, *Fasthealth. Garofano LHA*, in fact, opted to outsource all transportation.

Overall, the adjustment period from the traditional model to the unit-dose model took about 2 years and a half. The Health Direction is now happy of the results achieved and the doctors, as well as the nursing staff, were starting to get used to it and reaping the benefits. In the beginning, though, there were several critical points, such as:

- the considerable investment in technology to purchase equipment for the preparation of personalized therapies, for unpacking drugs, software, and hardware to manage the production process, consumables, tablets and laptops. The cost of the equipment for producing unit doses was € 650,000, the cost of the equipment for the computerized management of the stock was € 480,000, plus a maintenance contract for €180,000. Consumables for a 5-year production period were € 480,000.

- The need to organize training for doctors and nurses. Courses involved a 2-hour theory session and 5 hours of practice, with nurses and doctors tutored by ITs in the ward. Pharmacists were given a three-week training amounting to a total of 25 hours.

- Early resistance by nursing staff: often, doctors communicated prescriptions orally, leaving nurses the task of transcribing on paper. That activity, although it didn't fall within their duties, was however well accepted by nurses, who saw it as sign of confidence and esteem from the doctors. The introduction of computer-assisted prescription phased out the handwritten prescriptions, and at the beginning nurses felt bitter about this decision.

- Transfer of pharmacists: the 2 pharmacists from the smaller hospital had to be moved to the bigger one, with some on-call shifts. Production of unit-doses required 5 pharmacists, with the tasks of receiving prescriptions, check their consistency with the medical records in the computer system, and monitor the production of the therapy.

Despite these difficulties in the launch phase, Garofano LHA, after 6 years from the start of the project, seemed to be happy about the change, which had made it possible to achieve several good results in terms of:

- Integration among doctors and pharmacists.
- Improvement in the management of stock in the warehouse.
- Inventory reduction close to zero in wards.
- Optimize times, mostly to benefit nurses.
- Improvement in security.

Garofano LHA, then, set out an example Dr. Pietrafranca might have relied on in her negotiations with all the parties involved at Villandrea. However, that was not the case; in fact, it added another layer of uncertainty in her approach. Ideas were confused also because, in the last period, the Doctor had met some representatives from technology firms who presented her with all kinds of products and solutions. In particular, in the case of drug logistics, there were two possible alternatives to the unit-dose system:

– The computerized ward cabinet [10];
– The smart cart (see the box below for a brief description).

Box - The Smart Cart – A brief Description

The smart cart offers the rights solution for an effective management of clinical risk. It can be implemented in different clinical operations:

– Prescription of medical exams and drug therapies;
– Preparation and administration of drug therapies
– Monitoring vital signs
– Taking blood samples

The smart cart features a laptop computer connected to a device for monitoring the patient's vital signs. When administering the therapy, the nurse selects from the laptop the correct prescription and the cart gives access to the drugs listed in the prescription. The patient's safety and privacy are guaranteed, because the cart recognizes the nurse by a personal smart card, and protects sensible data thanks to the use of digital signature. Prescription, preparation, administration of the therapy are monitored from beginning to end, and the cart alarm signals if a risk for the patient has been detected (for example, the wrong drug has been picked).
The smart cart grants a complete rationalization of all the activities involved in hospital logistics because it can give a real time check on the goods stocked in the ward, highlight changes in consumption based on prescriptions and provides support in managing stock at the pharmacy.

Doctor Pietrafranca didn't have much confidence in these companies, as she had the distinct impression that their representatives had only the selling of their merchandise in mind; they didn't seem to have any real understanding of the LHA needs and were not able to offer solutions consistent with them. This was naturally a very crucial matter, and the Chief Medical Officer was aware of how important it is to develop partnership with business. However, she didn't know where to start (warehouse management, transport, technological solutions for drug logistics) and most of all she didn't know how to choose a suitable partner.

---

[10] Computerized ward closets, or smart closets, are made of a number of small trays where drugs are kept in dosage units. The smart closet is connected to a monitor and a keyboard: when the time for administering a specific drug comes, the nurses take from the closet the dosage units needed and put together the therapies tailored for each patient.

The First Meeting of the Logistics Innovation Team

Doctor Pietrafranca was curious about the mood of the staff at her LHA, she was wondering what people thought about the introduction of changes in logistics. She then called the first meeting of the team with the purpose of brainstorming ideas on the possible new directions for logistics.

After some initial of embarrassment, in particular by the pharmacists, who seemed to be in awe of doctors and nurses, the participants started to share some observations.

Doctor Pietrafranca wrote down every single passage from the brainstorming session. The following, however, are what had seemed to her as the most significant excerpts:

Pharmacist 1: "*Our job nowadays is not much different from that of ordinary warehouse workers, it's a shame we spend more time preparing carts for the ward than in checking the clinical consistency of prescriptions, which by the way we do not even have the chance to see. Our role should be to support doctors during the preparation of prescriptions … the right place for us is the ward, not the warehouse*".

Pharmacist 2: "*I am strongly against these rumors about centralizing the warehouse, not to speak of the proposal of having one single warehouse in the whole district, we have already talked about this proposal at SIFO (Italian Society of Hospital Pharmacies) meetings, and we pharmacists are prepared to challenge this measure in court*".

Nurse 1: "*Managing stock in the ward is a nightmare every week. We are frightened we might make a mistake with figures and to find ourselves without drugs when they are needed. A software to manage stocks would help us greatly in our job …*".

Pharmacist 1: "*Keeping track of stock in wards is quite challenging without the help of a computer software.*"

Nurse 2: "*One day I was feeling pretty exhausted and, while putting together the cart for administering therapies I picked the wrong drug. It had been a tough day, and the packaging of two different drugs were quite similar. Fortunately, while preparing the therapy I noticed I had picked the wrong drug, and I avoided a huge mistake. I've talked about what happened with my colleagues and together we decided to put these two drugs with similar packages on different shelves in the ward warehouse. Since then, I haven't mixed the two drugs up again. I think that, before spending money in technology and software, we should improve the way we are organized, using similar tricks.*"

Doctor 1: "*I totally agree, sometimes this reliance in technology and computers is inappropriate. Take the digital prescription, for instance. Writing a prescription is a moment of reflection for a doctor. At the hospital in Garofano LHA they have now computer prescriptions, each doctor has a tablet … I've spoken to the geriatrician there, and he told me that each prescription is a hassle: click, select, drag … and if you send the prescrip-*

tion by mistake, how can you go back? In my opinion, paper is still the most effective tool: you write, and if you make a mistake, you just draw a line, without any trouble".

Doctor 2 "That's right, sometimes you forget to write down when and how a certain drug is to be administered, but nowadays my nurses, who have been working with me for years, they know me well and know what to do ... if they are in doubt, they just ask me".

Nurse 1: "Innovation makes sense only if it gives us more time for the patient".

Logistics Manager: "We should implement industrial practices in managing our warehouses. For example, we have too much stock, we have a covering rate of more than two months (See Table 4), what prevents health authorities from working like car manufacturers, who have covering rates of just few days?"

Procurement Manager: "... I guess it is inevitable to think that logistics and purchases, in the medium term, should be managed directly by the District. We should get around to this and try, on the other hand, to find a way to have a say in the decisional process that is going on there. Finally, I take this opportunity to ask nurses to be more careful in the handling of goods in transit, it is important to check that the goods are consistent with the bill and, most of all, try not to lose the bills, to make the job of the Invoice office easier".

The Chief Medical Officer, going through her notes, was growing more and more worried, she hadn't been able to understand where to start, and, most of all, the thing that worried her most, she felt very little enthusiasm for the project among the people who had taken part in the meeting. In her view, those were the people who should have been part of the task force that had to lead the process of change of logistics in the whole authority.

Doctor Pietrafranca knew she had very little time; the CEO was waiting for accurate and detailed guidelines, as he needed to present Villandrea's project at the meetings where the re-organization of whole District was being discussed. The concrete risk was to be forced to accept models and choices made by others.

Table 4. Some figures on warehouse management at Villandrea LHA.

Item (in €)	2004	2005	2006
Average yearly stock	305,153	304,464	319,316
Total value outflow of goods with transit codes	4,633, 869	4,639,028	4,258,483
Total value outflow of goods without transit codes	1,401,767	1,486,213	1,758,251
Aggregate amount goods expired	9,812	8,917	9,670
Turnover rate	5	5	6
Covering rate	79	75	66

Source: author's elaboration.

Chapter 4
MODELS AND TOOLS

SUMMARY: 4.1. Lean Model. – 4.2. The Value-Based Health Care Model. – 4.3. Multidisciplinary Team – 4.4. – Focused Hospital. – 4.5. Patient profiles. – 4.6. Queueing analysis in healthcare.

4.1. Lean Model

In recent years, the health care sector has used quality improvement approaches and methodologies as an effort to meet efficiency, performance and quality improvement needs. Among these practices, lean has stood out in terms of diffusion in many hospitals. Lean is a strategy that focuses on meeting customer needs (i.e., patient, internal staff, organization) and continuously improving processes by optimizing flows, reducing waste, and creating value with the direct involvement of the organization's personnel. The adoption of lean requires the full awareness of the organization since a series of activities and processes need to be streamlined to add value to the customer, while activities that do not add value (i.e. waste) will be removed (Centauri et al., 2018).

The lean model includes a variety of different tools and models; (Mazzocato, 2007; Filligham, 2008; McLaughlin and Hays, 2008; Nicosia, 2010; Villa, 2012); however, according to the author, the following eight principles represent, in the case of healthcare sector, the main pillars of this approach:

1. Process management.
2. Visual mapping.
3. Elimination of wastes.
4. Control of Variability.
5. Just in Time production.
6. Kanban model (from «push» to «pull» approach).
7. Flows' separation.
8. Kaizen approach (continuous quality improvement).

1. Process management

In Paragraph 1.2 of this text, we have stressed the importance of starting from the concept of process: it is, in fact, important adopting a system-wide perspective with the final goal of improving the result for the final customer (either internal or external). Fragmented and partial solutions aimed to improve single pieces and activities of the entire process are, most of the times, useless and may bring unexpected negative results.

In healthcare delivery organizations, the actual sources of problems are, often, very far away from the place where the problems are recorded. For example the BMC case, illustrated in Chapter 2.5, shows that ED diversions and overcrowding are actually due to a bad scheduling of elective surgical cases.

Nicosia (2010) shows that projects aimed to increase productivity of the radiology may have, as a net effect, a deterioration of the efficiency for the entire healthcare chain since, due to the delays of the diagnostics activities, patients are kept longer in costly hospital settings (such as critical area).

As illustrated in Paragraph 1.6, a typical and quite effective way of representing a process is the flow-chart that graphically represents a process crossing actors (on the horizontal axis) and activities (on the vertical axis). Recently some lean experts (Guercini et al., 2016) recommend, as a tool of process mapping, the visual map that makes a distinction between front-line activities done directly to the patient and back-office ones.

2. Visual mapping

The visual mapping concept is an evolution of the process mapping: it is, in fact, not sufficient to have a static representation of the process but it is important to have real time information abouth the status of the process. In the case of patient flow logistics, for example, it is important to have real time information about the status of each patient and the next step in the diagnostic and treatment process.

According to Nicosia (2010) real time control of patient flows is essential in order to:

- maintain tension throughout the entire process;
- guarantee a timely process;
- identify all possible sources of waste;
- help identifying priorities;
- plan future changes.

3. Elimination of wastes

Once you have control (possibly in real-time) over the flow of activities, it is important to identify and eliminate all those activities that represent a waste, in fact any type of activity does imply a cost but not all activities bring an actual value to the process (see Figure 1).

Figure 1. Value-adding activities versus waste.

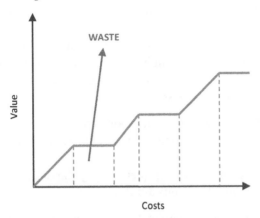

Source: author's elaboration.

Particularly lean literature has identified eight different types of waste illustrated in the following Table.

Table 1. Types of waste in the lean model.

WASTE	HEALTH SERVICE EXAMPLES
Waiting	Waiting for • patients, staff • results, prescriptions and medicine • doctors to discharge patients
Transportation	• Staff walking to the end of a ward to pick up notes • Central equipment stores for commonly used items instead of items located where they are used • Exams and clinical charts in continuous movement
Motion (moving around is not work)	• Unnecessary staff movement looking for paperwork • Storing syringes and needles at opposite ends of the room • Not having basic equipment in every examination room
Over processing	• Duplication of information • Asking for patients' details several times • Repeated clerking of patients
Over production	• Requesting unnecessary test • Keeping investigation slots "just in case" • Spare beds to keep up with peaks in the demand
Inventory	• Excess stock in warehouses that is not being used • Patients waiting to be discharged • Waiting lists
Correction	• Readmission because of failed discharge • Adverse drug reactions • Repeating tests because correct information was not provided

Source: adapted from Nicosia 2010 and Westwood et al. 2010.

The oversimplified representation of the surgical process depicted in Figure 2 illustrates two typical examples of waste: (i) waiting and (ii) over-processing.

As also illustrated in the incident of the patient Magboo (see Paragraph 1.7), waiting is a recurrent problem in the design and execution of healthcare delivery processes. Nicosia (2010), for example, makes several examples of waiting in the case of the diagnostics process:

(i)   We call 5-10 patients in a waiting room and we make them wait.
(ii) We perform the test (the only value-adding activity) that lasts no more than 30 minutes.
(iii) We ask patients to do another queue to pay the ticket.
(iv) We finally provide the results 3-5 days later.

Lean experts suggest to completely switch the perspective and to adopt the so-called "one-piece-flow" method: patients arrive at different period and complete – once a time – the all process; once the process is completed it is possible to move to the next one. This model allows better levels of satisfaction for the patients and increases organization' productivity.

Figure 2. Two examples of waste in the surgical process.

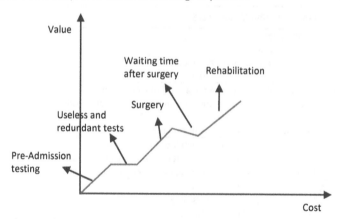

Source: author's elaboration.

4. Control of variability

The emphasis on process standardization represents another keystone of the lean approach. The latest manuals and articles, in fact, refer often to the terminology "*lean six-sigma*" where sigma stands for standard deviation; the goal is to outline the relevance of reducing process variability in order to eliminate the probability of deviations from the standard. We have extensively discussed, in this text, about control variability in the design and execution of healthcare production processes but we have, also, stressed the importance of making a distinction between natural and artificial variability. The so-called natural variability is a typical characteristic of healthcare production processes, it cannot be eliminated but needs to be optimally managed. The challenge for healthcare operations manager is deciding where to draw the line between natural variability and artificial variability.

5. Just in Time production

We have extensively discussed JIT model in the chapter 3 dedicated to supply chain management. According to the lean approach, an inventory represents a waste and, therefore, should be eliminated. In this sense, as already mentioned, the JIT allows, besides financial savings[1], the elimination of a series of costs related to space, technology and human resources dedicated to logistical activities. These models imply strong and reliable relationships with the suppliers that are required to bring supplies in a timely matter directly to the point of care.

However, it is advisable to manage these models with cautiousness considering the specificities of healthcare delivery processes (see Paragraph 1.3). Furthermore, as outlined in Paragraph 3.4, there is a series of conditions that need to be respected to create successful partnerships with external providers.

6. Kanban Model (from «push» to «pull» approach)

As we have described in Paragraph 1.2, any type of process is represented by a sequence of activities with a beginning, an end and a final output and outcome.

Typically, when you are done with a certain activity you need to "push" to move downstream the process. According to the Kanban model, it should be the other way around: the downstream activities should anticipate, thanks to a shared communication system, the requests coming from the upstream activities.

Some examples may help understanding this concept.

Think for example to the operating room block; we have seen (Par. 2.2)

---

[1] JIT models allow hospitals to reduce the financial resources' necessary to fund the purchasing of supplies.

that a typical OM performance indicator is the turnover time, that is the average time between interventions (patient gets out the OR and the next one gets in). This time is determined by the timeliness of cleaning operations between surgeries; the typical "push" approach would imply that, once you are done with the procedure, you call in the cleaning crew to sanitize the operating theatre. Alternatively ("pull" approach) you set up a codified and shared information system that allow the cleaning crew to anticipate the request; Nicosia in his work (Nicosia, 2010) mentions the example of the sign "No stretcher in front of the OR" that, for all cleaning people, means that the OR is empty and need to be cleaned up.

Another good example of Kanban model is represented by the "beds board" software described in the BMC case (cfr. Par. 2.5): with this software, ED staff does not need to push hospital floors to provide information about beds' availability, but this type of information is shared, on real time, throughout all the hospital units.

As for Supply Chain Processes, a good example of Kanban model is represented in the pictures below. The white shelfs on the left represent the weekly consumption of supplies (e.g. medicines or medical devices) while orange shelfs represent the spare items for another week. Once you are done with the consumption for the week you move the items stored on the right orange shelfs to the left and scan the white bar codes moving them out of the closet (see Figure 3). The central WH is organized in the same way with the shelfs of the same size of the ward so the replenishment process is easy and fast.

Figure 3. The Kanban model applied to the SCM process.

Source: author's pictures at a hospital floor. The picture has been taken during a project of SCM assessment conducted by CERISMAS (Research Centre in Healthcare Management), Università Cattolica del Sacro Cuore.

7. Flows' separation

As already seen in the current text, in order to improve patient flow logistics, it is possible to separate patient flows according to different criteria, like:

– *Scheduled cases vs. unscheduled cases*
As seen in Paragraph 2.1, emergency unscheduled cases are typically less variable and more predictable than elective cases. This allows to carefully estimate the capacity to set aside to create a dedicated physical pathway for urgencies/emergencies.
– *Age*
As illustrated in the figures below elderly behave differently and, typically, they tend to stay much longer at the hospital compared to other age clusters. This data paves the way to the creation of hospital settings entirely dedicated to patients aged 65 or over like: (i) ortho geriatric units[2] or (ii) post-acute care setting for fragile patients.

Figure 4. Average length of stay across different age clusters.

	0-14	15-44	45-64	65-74	>75
A	5,61	5,95	7,79	8,24	9,33
B	4,32	3,82	6,11	7,81	7,96
C	2,96	4,80	9,57	9,86	13,92
D	3,95	4,86	7,15	7,15	8,92
E	4,53	4,96	8,08	9,97	9,96
F	3,40	3,31	6,33	7,52	8,54
G	2,34	4,93	8,68	9,17	10,28
H	6,08	5,68	8,12	7,97	8,91
I	5,70	7,27	8,26	10,08	12,24
K	3,87	4,80	8,54	8,95	9,01

Source: adapted from Villa S., 2015 presentation at patient flow community [3], Milano, 12 Febbraio 2015.

---

[2] In this case, we refer to the situation of elderly patients that, after an orthopedic surgery, are treated in a multidisciplinary unit jointly managed by general medicine doctors, geriatrics and orthopedics.

[3] Patient flow community is a network of health care delivery organizations (founded in 2005) interested in benchmarking analyses of patient flow logistics. Now this network is jointly managed by CERISMAS (Università Cattolica del Sacro Cuore) and the Center for Healthcare Administration (Università degli Studi di Milano).

Figure 5. Percentage of bed blockers (patients with length of stay longer than thirty days).

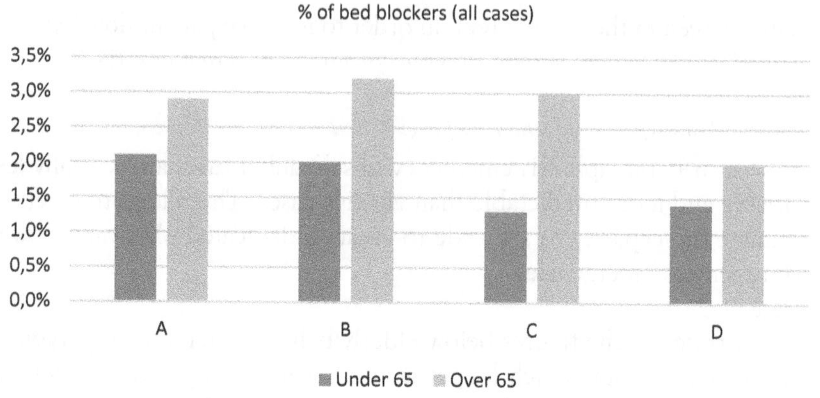

% of bed blockers (all cases)

■ Under 65   ■ Over 65

Source: adapted from Villa (2020) Presentation at CERISMAS Performance Lab, 30th November 2020.

– *Length of stay*

As indicated in the Paragraph 2.4 dedicated to the patient-centered model, it is possible to redesign patient flow logistics around expected length of stay, for example:

(i) Creation of a week surgery unit for surgical patients with an expected length of stay shorter than five nights. The data from patient flow community show that, on average, for a general multi specialties hospital this share of patients rounds, on average, around 40%.

(ii) Constitution of a post-acute care setting for patients that need to stay at the hospital more than 14 days (around 10% of the entire patient population).

– *Clinical and nursing complexity*

It is also possible to calibrate human and technological resources based on the nursing complexity and clinical complexity of each patient. In this case, however, it is important to establish clear criteria to get IN and get OUT these setting to guarantee an appropriate use of hospital assets avoiding chaotic situations as the one depicted in the case of BMC (see Chapter 2.5).

– *Separation between first visit and follow-up visit*

Some hospitals (Tomassini, 2019) have adopted the open access model for the scheduling of outpatient visits. The model builds upon the separation between first visits and follow-up visits. Particularly, for the first visits, there is no need to book the visit: patients are managed on first-come first-served basis and visited in a two-days' time span.

– *Covid Patients*

During the current pandemic crisis, a typical criterion for separating patients is the positivity to the virus COVID-19. Healthcare delivery organizations have set-up separated pathways for these patients at ED, have created wards for COVID patients or entire facilities according to the focused hospital model described in the next Paragraph.

8. Kaizen approach (continuous quality improvement)

Lean principles and tools build upon the continuous improvement framework developed back in the 50s by the automotive manufacturer Toyota. The Japanese word *"kaizen"*, in fact, is the merge of two words "kai" that means continuously and *"zen"* that means improvement.

This framework is the result of a series of principles that, in many cases, represents common sense, like:

1. Continuous involvement of personnel in quality improvement projects.
2. Side by side training run by high performance to low performance employees.
3. Continuous attention to internal and external client.
4. Continuous chase of ideas and opinions from all the employees regardless their role and function.
5. Managers – even top ones – are required to spend a fair amount of time "in the shopping floor" to observe how things are actually get done (the so called *gemba*).

Two simple tools commonly used to operationalize these principles are:

(i) the A3 report (see Figure 6) a way to collect ideas and change plans from all employees in the organization.
(ii) the idea board, a quite intuitive way to check the status of each idea/project (see Figure 7).

Figure 6. Example of A3 report.

Name of the project	Team	Contact email:
Description of the problem	Description of the project	
Current situation		
	Goals	

Source: author's elaboration.

Figure 7. The idea board.

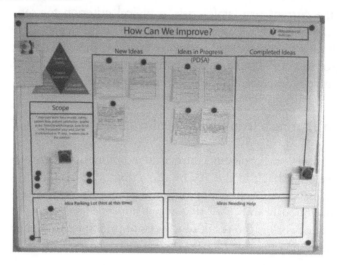

Source: this is a picture taken during a study tour at the UMASS Memorial Hospital (Worchester, Massachusetts, USA) carried out within the Fulbright-Funded project "Organizational responsibilities and performance indicators for hospital operations management" carried out at Boston University Questrom Business School in the academic year 2017-2018.

Conclusions

As briefly illustrated in this paragraph, the lean approach offers a series of effective and user-friendly tools and models to streamline and optimize healthcare operations. However, not all healthcare organizations have been capable to successfully implement, and maintain in the long run, this lean thinking approach.

Scientific literature agrees on the evidence that, a critical condition for the successful implementation of lean is the adoption of a system-wide perspective. Particularly, as sustained in the article written with the colleagues Centauri, Marsilio and Mazzocato (Centauri et al., 2018) it is important to:

1. Integrate lean into the organizational long-term strategic planning and include lean-related goals in the annual budget. In this way, the organizations strategy is translated into operational actions and professionals' efforts are better coordinated towards the identified goals.
2. Set-up a clear responsibility system with well-defined lean goals attributed to people and teams.
   For example, the three "lean" hospitals included in the study conducted with the colleagues Centauri, Marsilio and Mazzocato (Centauri et al.,

2018) have created central lean roles to develop strategic top-down projects, coordinate and provide internal training, and support bottom-up projects development. Another critical aspect is represented by the top management interest, engagement and support in the implementation process of lean.

3. Include lean into professionals' thinking and action. Lean is a powerful tool to favour the transition to process-based and patient cantered models of care since it favours the development of multiprofessional and multi-disciplinary team work. In those hospitals that have adopted lean, health care professionals had to learn how to coordinate their efforts and work together.

4. Integrate lean projects with clinical pathways. In other words, it is important that lean helps streaming clinical processes that should be designed and executed on the basis of evidence-based guidelines. This concept is very well exemplified by the words of a Medical department head nurse "... *Clinical pathways identify the patient flow from a clinical point of view, whereas lean practices contextualize clinical pathways into the specific organizational context ...*" (Centauri et al., 2018: 67). In this perspective, lean has been perceived, by many clinicians, as a tool to facilitate the implementation of clinical pathways in the daily clinical operations.

If we can find, in the scientific literature, several contributions about the most critical organizational conditions to successfully implement lean, still there is scant evidence about the actual impact of this type of innovations on hospital's performance and mainly limited to north America case studies.

For example, Virginia Mason Medical Center in Seattle, Washington, one of the earliest lean healthcare pioneers, increased productivity by 44% and saved between $12 million and $15 million in budgeted capital, after the first two years of lean adoption in 2004 (Bohmer and Ferlins, 2005). Legacy Emanuel Medical Center in Portland, Oregon, also initiated its lean improvement by involving nurses, doctors, and all support services to improve the movement of patients from one part of the process to the next. The hospital achieved improved clinical team time with patients, and 90% reduction in overall divert hours in 2009. Lean thinking at Contra Costa Regional Medical Center, California, reduced temporary staff level from 6 to 5 due to increased efficiency, and as a result, the medical center saved $66,000 in 2014.

Several survey researches report performance consequences of lean adoption. Using data from the 2017 National Survey of Lean/Transformation Performance Improvement in Hospitals, Shortell et al. (2018) document a positive relationship between lean adoption and self-reported measures of performance, including "eliminating waste in two or more processes or departments," "reducing medical errors," and "increasing throughput in the ED."

Combing the data used by Shortell et al. (2018) and Centers for Medicare & Medicaid Services data on hospital performance Po et al. (2019) find that lean adoption is negatively associated with the percentage of patients who left the ED without being seen and positively associated with earnings before interest, taxes, depreciation, and amortization (EBITDA) margin. Findings by Po et al. (2019) suggests a strong relationship between lean adoption and profitability.

4.2. The Value-Based Health Care Model

As said in Paragraph 1.1 the key challenge of the modern healthcare systems is to keep up with the demand and expectations of patients with shrinking available resources.

In this regard, a wide debate has recently developed around the concept of Value Creation – intended as clinical outcome achieved per resources used – which has become a focus of attention for all healthcare stakeholders (e.g. health care providers, industries, policy makers, etc.) especially in some Countries such as US and Scandinavian countries.

As sustained by the pioneristic works of Michael Porter (Porter, 2008) the value creation is possible only if providers organize their delivery model around a medical condition and provide services that consider the so-called "full cycle of care" with an integrated approach that considers all the different patients' needs.

Figure 8. The key principles of the value-based health care model.

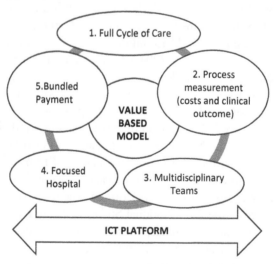

Source: author's elaboration.

As represented in the Figure 8, the value health care model suggests re-designing the organization of healthcare delivery around five key principles: (i) Full Cycle of Care; (ii) Process measurement (costs and clinical outcome); (iii) Multidisciplinary Teams (iv) focused hospital and (v) Bundled Payment.

The value-based healthcare model sustains that it is important to overcome the current architecture of the healthcare system still organized around specialties, departments, interventions, and individual facilities, when the value is actually created in the total care of a patient's medical condition over the **full cycle of care**. For any medical condition, such as a headache or breast cancer, there is a cycle of care that involves a long series of activities stretching across months and, perhaps, even years. Rather than building practice units that integrate the talent and facilities required to deliver outstanding care over the care cycle, hospitals and physician groups tend to remain organized along the lines of traditional academic specialties – radiology, anesthesiology, surgery. This not only ensures a disjointed experience for the patient, but makes difficult coordination and communication among the providers. (Porter, 2008).

Putting the clinical condition at the center of the organization means necessarily being able to produce **performance measures (cost and outcome) linked to the overall care process**. The measurement of outcome indicators along clinical pathways allows to obtain more valid and accurate information about the actual quality of care delivered to patients and provide more useful insights about the actual impact on costs and clinical outcomes of different organizational models.

As illustrated in Figure 8, this implies a deep redesign of the information systems that are, currently, vertically organized and completely unfit to provide timely and reliable info along the different phases of the whole process of care.

The value-based health model sustains the critical importance of **multidisciplinary teams** or Integrated Practice Units. A multi-disciplinary team is a group of different professionals (e.g. doctors and nurses) belonging to different specialties and specializations that share knowledge for the care of the same patient. In the current context (see Infra), a patient who is getting elder, more complex, with co-morbidities and chronic diseases can hardly find all the answers he/she seeks within a single specialty or professional.

Furthermore, in literature exists robust evidence (Andreatta, 2010; Atwal & Caldwell, 2005; Vliet Vlieland, 2004; Stephens et al. 2006; Pillay et al. 2016) that shows how the creation of Multidisciplinary Teams, dedicated to a specific medical condition or to homogeneous groups of diseases, determines a better use of resources, lower costs and also an improvement of clinical outcomes.

Finally, the **focused factory model** claims that the presence of resources and spaces dedicated to the realization of a specific product/service allows efficiency and quality improvements.

Applying this concept to healthcare implies organizing resources (human, technological and logistic) around single care problems (e.g. diabetes, breast cancer, hemophilia or onco-hematological diseases) with the creation of competence centers or focused hospitals (eg cancer center, orthopedics center, headache center, oncological hematology center) that focus the attention on the treatment and care of aggregated groups of patients with similar diagnosis or care needs. In his work (Hyer et al., 2009) Hyer and colleagues have identified four different dimensions to measure the degree of focus of a healthcare delivery organization:

(i)   Resources (human and technical) dedicated to the processing of a specific clinical condition.
(ii) Well-defined spaces within clear physical boundaries dedicated to a specific healthcare production process.
(iii) Specific procedures and guidelines for each single process of care for a group of patients with similar care needs.
(iv) Presence of an organizational infrastructure (e.g., planning and control system) designed around clinical conditions.

During the current pandemic, many healthcare organizations have dedicated spaces and resources to COVID-19 patients replicating, in this way, the focused factory model included in the value-based healthcare model.

In order to effectively implement the solutions described so far, two contextual conditions must be respected:

1. Policy-makers need to start paying for care cycles, not for discrete interventions. This will require bundled reimbursement for medical conditions. Only, in this case, it is possible to align reimbursement with value creation.
2. Data systems should be completely redesigned since, still, they are vertically organized and not designed around processes of care; the current information system is, thus, incapable to provide reliable and timely information on costs and outcome related to each clinical condition over the full cycle of care.

In the following two paragraphs we offer a specific focus on two elements of the value-based healthcare framework: (i) multidisciplinary teams (Paragraph 4.3) and (ii) focused hospital (Paragraph 4.4) analyzing the impact of these two innovations on the design of healthcare operations.

4.3. Multidisciplinary Team

Multidisciplinary team-working is a complex process that brings together a group of diverse health care professionals to work and share their expertise, knowledge, and skills in order to deliver patient services (Mitchell, Parker, Giles,&Boyle, 2014; Nancarrow et al., 2013). Evidence shows that multidisciplinary teams play a significant role in generating a wide range of benefits, such as increased learning and development of people and institutions, better resource utilization, minimization of unnecessary costs, improvements in job performance and work quality, and more efficacious outcomes for patients and their families (Andreatta, 2010; Atwal & Caldwell, 2005).

The scientific literature (Friedland et al., 2011; Marsilio et al., 2017; Villa et al., 2020) identifies two different possible interpretations of the concept of multidisciplinary approach, namely:

(i) The sharing of the clinical decision-making process between different medical and allied health specialties.
(ii) The physical compresence of different healthcare professionals at the bedside of the patient.

The first scenario does not require the simultaneous physical presence of physicians, but rather it involves only the clinical decisions making process and, therefore, can be easily managed remotely using virtual platforms.

On the contrary, joint visits of the same patient by several professionals requires rethinking of the operations management system in terms of modifying the lay-out, reorganizing the flow of activities and redesigning the scheduling system.

This latter interpretation of multidisciplinary work calls for a sharp redesign of the healthcare delivery processes but, a the same time, is capable to guarantee relevant improvements of quality of care.

For example, a study regarding patients in the South and Central Bronx affected by obesity and diabetes has described the approach that has been implemented which involves patients attending, on the same day, one-to-one visits with a multidisciplinary team. During these visits, each patient individually meets each member of the team and each member shares specific and relevant information about the patient. The study has highlighted the importance of this approach showing a reduction of repetition of critical health messages as well as improving the psychosocial experience of the patients with higher levels of satisfaction (Malkin-Washeim et al., 2017)

Another interesting study is the one conducted by Friedland and colleagues (2011) that analysed the outcomes of 726 cases of primary head and neck cancer patients including those managed in the multidisciplinary clinic or team setting (MDT) and those managed outside of an MDT by individual disciplines (non-MDT) in the same institution. The study shows an improvement both in terms of clinical outcome (5-year survival) and process management (synchronous chemotherapy and radiotherapy) for patients enrolled in the multidisciplinary clinical pathway compared to those who were not enrolled.

Despite these promising results, there are several barriers that prevent the full realization of multidisciplinary approach; such barriers include the lack of adequate infrastructures, online availability of diagnostics, which allows the traceability of any different medical opinion, cost and time constraints. Suter et al.'s (2009) review has reported some key limits to an efficient information integration: poor technology solutions, lack of well-designed electronic information systems and shared standards. The study conducted with Marsilio and Torbica (Marsilio et al., 2017), after an empirical analysis of the adoption of the transcatheter aortic valve (TAVI)[4], proves that, to effectively adopt a multidisciplinary approach, it is important to act coordinately on more dimensions such as (a) shared layouts and spaces that cross the boundaries of the specialized health care units, (b) standardization of the core processes through the implementation of local clinical pathways, (c) structured knowledge management mechanisms and (d) planning and budgeting systems that incorporates the multidisciplinary concept.

4.4. Focused Hospital

The focus idea was originally introduced in the manufacturing sector by Skinner (1974), he coined the concept of "focused factory" suggesting that organizing the production plant "on a limited, concise, manageable set of products, technologies, volumes and markets" can lead to higher productivity and quality. At that time the major problem was to reduce complexity within production processes and realize an organizational structure more flexible in order to meet the market demand (Bozarth, 1993).

Skinner (1974), in his work, doesn't limit the focus to the only narrow range of activities but underlines that it is given by the design of the plant, the processes and infrastructure around the focus objective. This concept has been successfully implemented in industrial sector and today it is widespread along manufacturing company leading to important competitive

---

[4] TAVI is a highly technological, complex, and intensive procedure for the treatment of aortic stenosis in elderly or high-risk patients that requires the contemporary presence of cardiologists, cardiac surgeons, technicians and nurses.

benefits (Vokurka and Davis, 2000); however also in healthcare context it has been recognized by literature how implementation of a focused strategy allow healthcare organizations to provide care at higher quality and lower cost (cfr. Value-Based Healthcare) (Ginsburg, 2000; Kumar, 2010).

The focus concept in healthcare is closely associated with patient aggregation strictly connected to the idea that economies can be realized, clinical outcomes and patient service improved by grouping patients with similar needs (Villa et al. 2009, Rafiqu et al., 2019).

Herzlinger (1997) in her manuscript underlines as in hospitals there are rooms to improve focus in operations considering it as one of the key sources towards is it possible to reduce the efficiency gaps in healthcare delivery. She describes focused hospitals as multidisciplinary organizations based on common goals (e.g. the treatment of specific patient groups), organized and managed to concentrate the attention on specific surgical procedures or to specialize on particular diseases. In this early Herzlinger's definition, there is a "call for a change" from the old professional-centered model to a patient-centered (and process-centered) organizations, moreover she seems to recognize focus as a "key" to focalize hospitals operations and improve efficiency (Terwiesch, 2011).

Few studies (Herzlinger, 1997; Hyer et al., 2009; McDermott and Stock, 2011; Terwiesch C., 2011; Cook at al., 2014; Capkun et al., 2012) have also tried to empirically test the impact of the focus approach on hospital performance.

The operationalization of a focused strategy has allowed healthcare organizations to improve performance regarding both quality and effectiveness of care; various studies have proved the positive effects of focus on operational performance, such as length of stay or throughput time, but also about outcomes indicators including mortality rate, hospital readmissions, complications and so on (Kumar and Nunne, 2008; Ding, 2015).

Literature identifies three main types of focus that lead to different organizational models, namely:

- Specialty hospital (S. Kumar, 2010): hospital with a strong focus on a specific specialty or medical discipline (e.g. orthopedic Institute or cancer center).
- Service lines: hospitals that have a high specialization on a specific surgical or medical procedure within an organizational unit (e.g. Coronary angioplasty and stents or Day Surgery).
- Care Center or Comprehensive Care Center: autonomous institutions or parts of larger organizations (General hospitals) with a focus on specific medical condition (e.g. Hernia Center, Integrated trauma Unit, Headache Center or hemophilic center).

When general hospitals decide to emphasize the focus, they tend to create internally a "focused hospital unit" or "focused center" (N.L. Hyer et al, 2009). The latter can be qualified as independent organizations that are part of larger organizations (General hospitals) with a specific focus on similar medical conditions (e.g. Cancer Center, Stroke center) or patient groups (e.g. Trauma Center, Ambulatory Surgery Centers) (Pratt, 2008).

These types of focused centres are associable to the concept of "plant within a plant" introduced by Skinner (1974). The creation of a "plant within a plant" is attributable to an organization that emphasizes the focus of a hospital division (Huckman and Zinner, 2008) emphasizing, to such a degree, the constitution of a new plant recognized in a "focus center" (Pratt, 2008).

The care centres are hospital units located within the hospital campus but, at the same time, are administratively separate and managed as autonomous organizations or separate business units (Yang et al. 1992); frequently the implementation of an emphasis strategy lead to the creation of more than a focus center enabling general hospital to generate a multiple focused-factory plant (Pieters et al. 2010). Studies regarding care centers found statistical significance regarding both operational and financial performance improvement (Pratt, 2008).

Finally, general hospital can opt to emphasize focus on a single service line, medical or surgical procedure (Liedtka and Whitten, 1998; Peltokorpi et al. 2016).

Possible examples, in this sense, are represented by the creation of a lab dedicated to Coronary Angioplasties or a building entirely dedicated to day surgery or ambulatory surgeries (Eastaugh, 2014).

Based on the evidence found in scientific literature, the focus on a single procedure allows relevant increases in efficiency and productivity mainly due to economies of scale and learning (Turnipseed, 2007; Pass et al., 2008; Capkun et al., 2012).

Some authors (Vogeli et al., 2007; Porter, 2008; Nolte & McKee, 2008; Villa et al., 2020), sustain that the focused hospital is an effective organizational model for the management of chronic disease whose burden represents one of the most important challenges for the healthcare systems of developed countries.

In this perspective, in fact, the focused hospital model should provide, to **homogeneous categories of chronic patients**, an integrated and multidisciplinary approach which includes screening, check-ups, monitoring and coordinating treatment and patient education.

The literature outlines some examples of good practices in the design and management of focused hospitals.

As said, one of the first and most known experience of focused hospital is the Shouldlice hospital a hospital in Canada focused on hernias.

Porter (2008) often mentions the case of the West German Headache Center, a facility entirely dedicated to patients with migraine with teams of doctors (neurologists, physical therapists and psychologists) called Integrated Practice Units (IPU) dedicated to the management of this specific subgroup of patients. The center benefits of a dedicated administrative structure and it can rely on some beds for possible hospital admissions. The center is also linked, through an electronic platform, to other specialties working in other facilities.

Villa and colleagues (2020) describe, in their work, the model of the Comprehensive Care Center (CCC) dedicated to hemophilic patients. Hemophilia is a complex chronic congenital bleeding disorder linked to the lack of coagulating factor.

This CCC works as focused hospital guaranteeing:

(i)   specialised medical expertise in congenital bleeding disorders available 24 hours a day;
(ii) dedicated laboratories that respect the European quality standards especially regarding emergency diagnosis;
(iii) access to all specialties required for an integrated and multidisciplinary management of haemophilic patients;
(iv) management of innovative drugs and drugs availability;
(v)   adequate physicians to patients ratio.

Laratro and Villa (2020), in their work, illustrate also the experience of the center for oncological hematologic patients at Torino Local Health Authority. In this case we have a physical facility entirely dedicated to a homogenous subgroup of patients with the following assets: (i) 18 ambulatories; (ii) beds for day hospital admissions or regular admissions (iii) dedicated diagnostic lab and (iv) a dedicated pharmacy. Furthermore, the center can rely upon a multidisciplinary team of doctors that meet on a weekly basis and they are connected, through a telemedicine system, with other specialists working in other facilities.

Rafiq and coullegues (2019) in their work describe an integrated center dedicated to patients with multiple chronic conditions (MCC) of diabetes, cardiovascular and kidney diseases. This center was established at a tertiary academic medical hospital, Danderyd University Hospital, in Stockholm, Sweden. The hospital is a large Emergency Hospital, with 540 beds, that provides specialist health services for approximately 650,000 persons as well as conducting research and teaching as an affiliated teaching hospital of Karolinska Institutet.

The goal of the center is to offer comprehensive care to patients in an integrated, multidisciplinary, and person-centered manner to improve care coordination, reduce and replace visits to a variety of doctors and nurses, and, within a period of one-year, develop sustainable care management plan that can be handed-off to primary care.

The center operates on weekdays during office hours. HND Staff is a team of health-care professionals including the junior consultant and a nurse manager supported by an "undersköterska", an equivalent of an American Licensed Practical Nurse (LPN) or a British NHS Health-Care Assistant. This team is complemented with dieticians, physiotherapists, part-time nurses specialized in heart failure, nephrology and diabetes, and two each of nephrologists, cardiologists and endocrinologists on a rotating schedule. Instead of patients visiting the different specialties at different locations as in traditional care model, the HND center is designed from a patient-centered perspective where patients obtain all necessary treatments at a single location (Rafiq et al., 2019: 1077).

Despite the growing interest around the focused-factory model, it is still critical achieving a better understanding of the actual impact of this model on the overall quality of care.

In order to do so it is important to develop a common knowledge about the main features of a focused hospital.

As mentioned earlier in this paragraph, Hyer and colleagues (2009) have proposed four dimensions to measure the intensity of a focused hospital: (i) Resources; (ii) Space; (iii) Processes; (iv) Organizational Infrastructure.

In a recent study (Laratro and Villa, 2020) we have used this framework to further spell out the operational dimensions of a focused hospital across the four perspectives identified by Hyer and colleagues.

We believe this work is very much important because it helps future studies to better understand the actual impact of innovation in the redesign of organization of care. It is widely documented, in scientific literature, that in healthcare management it is usually quite difficult establishing clear relationships of cause and effect because of (i) the difficulty of measuring quality of care and (ii) the presence of a quite long list of confounding variables. However, the analysis of the impact of managerial innovations in healthcare can also be distorted by the actual level of the intensity of the change implemented. In other words, a hospital that claims to be organized according to the principles of patient-centered model is actually organizing all the wards in a flexible and multidisciplinary manner or a "lean" hospitals has actually redesigned all processes with these new logics?

In the case of a focused hospital – through the analysis of six different cases – we have come up with a list items that actually identify the degree of intensity of "focus" in the organization of hospital care.

Resources

– Dedicated multidisciplinary teams.
– Specialized professionals.
– Codified standards of knowledge and skills.
– ICT solutions to support clinical decision making process.
– Drugs distribution managed directly by the center.

Spatial

– Clear definition of physical boundaries of the care center.
– Integrated services (e.g. laboratory, pharmacy, blood bank) within the plant.
– Dedicated spaces (e.g. dedicated ambulatories).
– Dedicated technology (e.g. imaging).

Processes (clinical and administrative)

– Standardization of activities.
– Implementation of a clinical pathway[5].
– Accreditation of the center by international bodies.
– Presence of formalized network linked with the primary care sector.
– Management of the full cycle of care within the Center.
– Shared medical appointments where the patient can see different specialists.

Organizational Infrastructure

– Front-office to help patients in their routine activities (e.g. booking a visit or an exam).
– Formalized position of the clinical director.
– Constitution of a responsibility center.
– Efficiency and outcome indicators measured around the clinical condition.

Defining a score to measure the actual intensity of a given change is definitely a useful tool especially when analyzing innovation in public sector where both managers and policy makers tend to take advantage of the so-called boomerang effect, that is, they announce an innovation – in order to gain immediate consensus – even if the actual change is still to come.

---

[5] For a clear definition of clinical pathway we refer the reader to Paragraph 1.5.

4.5. Patient Profiles

A key prerequisite for the construction of a focused hospital is represented by the possibility of grouping patients with similar needs.

It must be noted, however, that within a group of patients affected by the same clinical condition, it is possible to find different needs that will call for a different intensity of care with the involvement of different professionals.

An interesting study conducted by Van Dijk and colleagues (2013) has, for example, outlined the importance of identifying different patient profiles in the design and implementation of disease management programs (DMPs) for diabetic patients. Particularly the study, using different criteria such as age, type of medication and healthcare utilization in primary care, has identified three main broad categories of diabetic patients.

On the other hand, Kucukyazici and coullegues (2011) have proved the importance of patient charateristics as a relevant confounding variable in assessing the impact of different patterns of care for stroke patients discharged by hospitals.

Finally, some studies (Jamison et al. 1994 and Turk and Rudy 1998) have proved that a better patients' profiling can lead to a more effective chronic pain management among oncologic and terminally ill patients. Particularly, these authors suggest to adopt a more multi-dimensional approach including measures such as activity interference, emotional distress, pain intensity.

In conclusion, findings in the literature suggest that the adoption of a classification aimed at grouping patients in profiles according to different factors and characteristics, can lead to better outcomes in the delivery of appropriate and customized treatment for different types of disease.

In the case of heart diseases, the development of a subjective classification system based on the severity of the disease, the so-called "INTER-MACS patient profiles", has contributed to improving the resolution of patients' outcomes in advanced stages of heart failure.

Another interesting case study is hemophilia disease (Villa et al., 2019).

As a chronic congenital bleeding disorder, patients with hemophilia have special needs for long-term, lifelong management. Primary and secondary prophylaxis is needed to avoid or delay progression of arthropathy and improve the quality of life. Management of hemophilia has also become more complex in recent years due to the development of newer agents for prophylaxis and on-demand replacement therapy.

Within this group of patients, however, the intensity of care varies significantly based on the simultaneous presence of other possible comorbidities such as the presence of inhibitors, arthropathies or infections. In a study conducted with other colleagues (Villa et al., 2019) triangulating the analysis of clinical data and the results of direct observation, we have identified eight different type of patients (see Table 2).

Table 2. Examples of classification of patients with emophilia.

1.	previously untreated patient with known family history
2.	previously untreated patient with unknown family history
3.	paediatric, severe, positive inhibitor
4.	paediatric, mild, negative inhibitor
5.	paediatric, moderate, negative inhibitor
6.	adult/elderly, severe, moderate and mild, positive inhibitor, arthropathy, co-infections
7.	adult/elderly, severe and moderate negative inhibitor
8.	adult/elderly, mild negative inhibitor

Source: adapted from Villa et al. (2020).

These eight patient categories – all hemophilic patents – are characterized by a different level of intensity of care. For example, an elderly patient who is positive for inhibitor, and with arthropathy and coinfection, undergoes an average of 8 hematologic examinations yearly, he is followed by other several other specialists and goes through a specific series of testing.

Another interesting project of patient profiling is the one carried out at the European Oncological Center where, through Artificial Intelligence algorithms, they have set-up a patients' profiling system before surgical intervention. The model classifies patients population based on:

– minor complications;
– middle and serious complications;
– need of hospitalization after surgery;
– expected length of stay;
– recovery after 12 months.

This info helps manager to plan in advance and design more coherent and efficient healthcare delivery processes.

4.6. Queueing analysis in healthcare

Many organizations, such as banks, airlines, telecommunications companies, and police department, routinely use queueing models to help determine capacity levels needed to respond to demand in a timely fashion.

Though queueing analysis has been used in hospitals and other healthcare settings, its use in this sector is not widespread.

Yet, given the pervasiveness of delays in healthcare and the fact that many healthcare facilities are trying to meet increasing demands with tightly constrained resources, queueing models can be very useful in developing more effective policies for bed allocation and staffing, and in identifying other opportunities for improving service. Queueing analysis is also a key tool in estimating capacity requirements for possible future scenarios, including demand surges due to new viruses, diseases or acts of terrorism.

In this perspective, these models are very useful to better manage the demand's variability linked to the current COVID-19 pandemic.

In this text we will not provide all the technicalities and computational algorithms to carry out queuing calculations, but we will describe only the basic principles and the underlying assumptions. For a thorough description of queuing calculations, we suggest to look at the work of Linda Green[6].

Queuing modelling helps to address one of the key goals of operations management that is filling the disparity between demand for a service and the capacity available to meet that demand. Often this mismatch is temporary and due to natural variability in the timing of demands and in the duration of time needed to provide service. It must be noted that queuing calculations are incapable to model artificial variability, that type of variability linked to misbehaviors of defects in the process organization.

A simple example would be a healthcare clinic where patients walk in without appointments in an unpredictable fashion and require anything from a flu shot to the setting of a broken limb. This variability and the interaction between the arrival and service processes make the dynamics of service system very complex.

In this type of scenario queueing model represents a powerful tool to establish how much capacity is needed to achieve some desired level of performance in terms of productivity and timeliness.

The rule that determines the order in which queued customers are served is called the queue discipline.

The most common discipline is the familiar first-come, first-served (FCFS) rule, but other disciplines are often used to increase efficiency or reduce the delay for more time-sensitive customers. For example, in an ED,

---

[6] Green L. (2006). "Queuing analysis in healthcare" in Hall R.W. "Patient Flow: Reducing Delay in Healthcare Delivery" Springer's International Series, Los Angeles and Green L. (2011). "Queueing Theory and Modeling." In *Handbook of Healthcare Delivery Systems*. Ed. Yuehwern Yih. London.

the triage system is an example of a priority queue discipline.

A queueing model is a mathematical description of a queueing system which makes some specific assumptions about the probabilistic nature of the arrival and service processes, the number and type of servers, and the queue discipline and organization.

Queueing models rely upon different assumptions (Green, 2006):

1. the system has been operating with the same arrival, service time and other characteristics for a sufficiently long time;
2. the probability distribution for the queue length and customer delay is independent of time;
3. the number of arrivals per unit of time has a Poisson distribution. The underlying basis of the Poisson assumption is that customers arrive at random at the given average rate.

In determining whether the Poisson process is a reasonable model for arrivals in a specific service system, it is useful to consider its three defining properties:

1. Customers arrive one at a time.
2 The probability that customer arrives at any time is independent of when other customers arrived.
3. The probability that a customer arrives at a given time is independent of the time.

In most contexts, customers generally do arrive one at a time. Though there may be events, such a major accident, that trigger multiple simultaneous arrivals, this is likely to be an exceptional circumstance which will not significantly affect the usefulness of this modeling assumption. For example, in an emergency room, where the population of potential patient is very large, it is unlikely that someone arriving with a broken arm has anything to do with someone else's injury or illness, or the fact that the number of patients who arrived between 9am and 10am provides information about the number of patients that are likely to arrive between 10 am and 11 am.

Again, there may be occasional exceptions, such as a flu outbreak, for which there is an exogenous factor responsible for generating multiple arrivals over a time period.

However, this assumption is still likely to be a reasonable one in most situations. The third property may be more suspect. In fact, as we have seen in this text patients' arrivals can vary across the days of the week but also across the hours of the day. However, it is possible to use the standard Poisson process as a model for a shorter interval of time during which the arrival rate is fairly constant.

In any case different studies (Kim et al., 1999, Green et al., 2005, Green, 2006 and 2011) have empirically shown that many arrival processes behave as a Poisson distribution.

Among these are demands for emergency services such police, fire and ambulance, arrivals to banks and other retail establishments, and arrivals of telephone calls to customer service call centers. Because of its prevalence and its assumption of independent arrivals, the Poisson process is the most commonly used arrival process in modeling service systems.

In healthcare, the Poisson process has been verified to be a good representation of unscheduled arrivals to various parts of the hospital including ICUs, ORs, obstetrics units and EDs.

The most commonly used queueing model is the M/M/s or Erlang delay model. This model assumes that there is a single queue, customers are served on a First Come First Served basis an they are processed into s identical servers[7].

If all these assumptions are met, in order to run the queuing model it is sufficient to know only three parameters:

1. *The number of servers*
   A "server" is the production unit (e.g., operating rooms or inpatient beds) or the person (e.g., a doctor in the ambulatory center). If all servers are busy upon a customer's arrival, they must join a queue.
2. *The number of arrivals in the period of time analyzed*
   This parameter, known as "arrival rate" and typically indicated with the letter "λ", is the expected number of arrivals per unit time. For example, if the system serves 10 customers per hour, then the expected number of arrivals, in any 60 minute interval, is 10 and the expected number to arrive in a 15 minute interval is 2.5. Notice that these are averages so they need not to be integer values.
3. *The Service Time (throughput time)*
   That is the elapsed time from the start of work on that unit to its completion, including waits and set-up time.

The queueing models allow to analyze the impact of the change of these

---

[7] There are several variations on the basic M/M/s queueing model. One important one for many healthcare organizations is the M/M/s with priorities. While the fundamental model assumes that customers are indistinguishable and are served FCFS, the priority model assumes that customers have differing time sensitivities and are allocated to two or more service classes I = 1, 2, ... N, and that customers are served in priority order. This type of model requires, however, few adjustments of the basic queuing model described in this paragraph.

parameters (number of servers, service time and arrival rate) on two different broad dimensions:

1. *Utilization rate* defined as the average number of busy servers divided by the total number of servers (Green, 2006). As explained in this text, productivity is a typical OM performance dimension; for example, scientific literature considers 85% as a good standard for beds' occupancy rate.
2. *Timeliness of the service* measured with indicators such as the probability that an arrival will experience a delay, or the average delay.

The queuing model has been actually used in the case of BMC (see Paragraph 2.5) to decide the number of ORs to dedicate to unscheduled urgent cases. In this case, we have used the basic model[8] considering that (i) patient arrivals looked like a Poisson distribution and (ii) the model adopted was the M/M/s illustrated earlier.

We used this model to the Menino Pavillon characterized by the following elements:

- Daily Number of unscheduled cases: 10.
- Mean arrival rate (N. of cases per hour) = 0.4 (given by the ratio of 10 by 24 – the hours in a day).
- Activity (Service) Time (in hours) = 2.5. This time includes all the time of the entire surgical process including the so-called set-up time that is the time necessary for the operations of cleaning and preparing the OR (see Paragraph 2.2).

The goal was, at that time, deciding the appropriate number of operating rooms to dedicate at urgent unscheduled cases finding a good balance between the overall operating rooms productivity and the capability of the system to deal with emergency / urgencies in a timely manner.

With these parameters, in fact, dedicating only one operating room to unscheduled cases lead to suboptimal results in terms of timeliness, for example (i) the probability of patients diverted (sent to other hospitals) was equal to 20% while (ii) the average wait for those patients who do wait was equal to five hours. On the other hand, dedicating two operating rooms to emergencies would lead the system to unsatisfactory results under an efficiency perspective (average OR utilization rate equal to 50%).

In order to find a better balance between timelines and efficiency, the hospital has acted on two different drivers:

---

[8] Readers interested in having the Excel spreadsheet used for these queueing calculations can e-mail directly the author: stefano.villa@unicatt.it.

- The management of the demand with a stricter control on the real nature of clinical emergencies.
- The reduction of the overall throughput time with managerial interventions such as the adoption of lean management techniques to reduce the set-up time.

The combined effect of the reduction of the overall service time and of the arrival rate (thanks to the elimination of cases that could be easily postponed after 24 hours) has allowed the hospital to achieve satisfactory results with only one operating room dedicated to urgent unscheduled cases.

This quick example explicates quite well challenges and complexities of managing operations in healthcare sector where it is not always straightforward finding the balance between different dimensions such as bed flexibility and quality of care, productivity and timeliness of care, and often differing perspectives from policymakers, managers, physicians, nurses and patients. To effectively address all these challenges, managers must be informed by operational and performance data and use these data in models to gain insights that cannot be obtained from experience and intuition alone.

CONCLUSION

Eugenio Anessi Pessina [1]

As explained extensively throughout the book, operations management (OM) can be viewed as the enabling mechanism which supports production processes. When applied to health care, in particular, it means managing and optimizing the flows of patients and goods across hospital production units by means of scheduling and capacity planning, organization of spaces, process design and execution, and information systems.

The OM function was first developed in the manufacturing industry. More recently, it has gained momentum also in health care, generating significant interest among health-care professionals, managers, policymakers, and academics. Indeed, OM provides a set of effective models, tools, and technical solutions to improve the quality and efficiency of health-care production processes. From this perspective, this book can be viewed as a particularly useful guide, as it provides the reader with a wide range of practical hints to implement innovative models such as the patient-centered model, lean thinking, or the focused hospital.

At the same time, this book is particularly valuable and fairly unique in that it analyses OM within a strong conceptual framework. Such framework highlights that OM does not operate in a vacuum. Rather, it needs to continuously pursue a consistency with the peculiar characteristics and constraints of a given organization.

Along these lines, the first chapter places a strong emphasis on the need for OM strategies in health care to deal with two key sets of constrains: on the one hand, the public ownership of most health-care delivery organizations; on the other, the specificities of health-care production processes. At the same time, the chapter warns against the instrumental reference to these constraints as an excuse to perpetuate existing defects and dysfunctions. Paragraph 1.5, for example, highlights the crucial distinction between natural and artificial variability. The former stems from the very nature of health-care processes and cannot be eliminated. The latter is caused by dysfunctional processes and should be removed through proper managerial interventions.

---

[1] Professor of Management, director of CERISMAS (Research Center in Healthcare Management) and coordinator of the PhD Program in Management and Innovation, Università Cattolica del Sacro Cuore.

In addition, the book makes continuous references to a system-wide approach. OM models and tools are not presented as the components of a self-contained function. Rather, great emphasis is placed on the need for understanding and managing the interdependences with the rest of the organization. For example, the conditions for a successful OM change plan are said to include:

- Consistency with the organization's strategic goals. For example, a niche hospital serving only a targeted number of service lines requires a different operations strategy from an acute care community hospital treating multiple service lines.
- A process perspective. Optimizing single pieces of the organization would lead to suboptimal results or, in some cases, even to a deterioration of the organization's overall performance.
- Consistency with the organizational infrastructure. A collaboration must be pursued with other key offices such as the senior medical leadership, planning and control, purchasing and logistics, and clinical governance.
- A performance management system capable of considering the needs and specificities of production processes and possibly including some key OM goals in the management control cycle.

At the time of writing, the Covid-19 pandemic is still ongoing. Under these circumstances, health-care OM systems have been facing three main challenges. The first is **responsiveness**, to deal with the peaks and troughs of the epidemiological curve. The second is **resilience**, with particular respect to the continuity of care that must be guaranteed at least to the most critical and fragile portions of the population, like oncological patients. The third is **restoration**, to learn from the pandemic and take advantage of the many worthy innovations that have been introduced to cope with it.

Undoubtedly, OM concepts and tools have been essential in the management of the pandemic. Examples include:

- **Timeliness and flexibility**. Hospitals need to carefully balance the trade-off between productivity and flexibility in order to cope with the demand fluctuations induced by the pandemic. In this respect, a new interesting concept is the "sleeping hospital", which is intended to provide spare capacity in order to meet the peaks of demand.
- **Multidisciplinarity.** Covid patients require a multidisciplinary approach – in fact, this applies to chronic patients in general. OM has played a key role in supporting a multidisciplinary and integrated approach to these patients through a redesign of lay-outs and processes.
- **Separation of flows.** As highlighted multiple times throughout the book, the concept of flows separation can be applied to various contexts (e.g., elderly care; hospital settings designed around the expected lengths

of stay; first vs. follow-up ambulatory visits). During the pandemic, this concept has been essential to protect non-Covid patients.

- **Focused hospital.** The focused factory model, analyzed in section 4.4, has been an effective way of separating Covid patients from all other patients.
- **Capacity planning.** During the pandemic, bed capacity has emerged as the most important bottleneck. It is, thus, particularly important to invest in bed capacity planning, also by taking advantage of innovative IT solutions.

Once the pandemic is over, OM can be expected to remain important, although challenges will change. Key issues will presumably include the developments of "digital health"; the redefinition of the skill mix (e.g., physicians v. nurses) in the provision of care; the increased role of primary care, home care, and preventive medicine; the management of chronic diseases; and the strengthening of interorganizational networks involving public and private providers operating in hospital and non-hospital settings.

REFERENCES

Ackroyd, S., Hughes, J.A., and Soothill, K. (1989). Public sector services and their management. Journal of Management Studies, 26 (6), 603-619.

Affleck, et al. (2013). Access block and emergency department overcrowding "Emergency Department Overcrowding and Access Block." CJEM 15 (6): 359-70. https://doi.org/10.2310.

Aiken, L., Sloane, D., Sochalski, J. (2002). Hospital nurse staffing and patient mortality, nurse burnout, and job dissatisfaction. JAMA The Journal of the American Medical Association 288-16: 1987-1993.

Airoldi, G., Brunetti, G., Coda, V. (2004). Corso di economia aziendale, Bologna, Il Mulino.

Alqahtani, A.R., Elahmedi, M.O. (2015). Pediatric Bariatric Surgery: The Clinical Pathway. Obesity Surgery, Vol. 25, 910-921.

Andreatta, P.B. (2010). A typology for health care teams. Health Care Management Review, 35(4), 345-354.

Anessi Pessina, E., Jommi, C., and Cantù, E., 2001. New funding arrangements in the Italian National Health Service. International Journal of Health Planning and Management, 16 (4), 47-68.

Aptel, O., and Pourjalali, H. (2001). Improving activities and decreasing costs of logistics in hospitals. A comparison of U.S. and French hospitals. The International Journal of Accounting, 36 (1), 65-90.

Arrowsmith, S. (1995). Public procurement as an instrument of public policy and the impact of market liberalisation. Law Quarterly Review, 111 (April), 235-284.

Asplin, B., et al. (2003). A Conceptual Model of Emergency Department Crowding, Ann Emerg Med. 2003; 42:173-180.

Atwal, A., and Caldwell, K. (2005). Do all health and social care professionals interact equally: A study of interactions in multidisciplinary teams in the United Kingdom. Scandinavian Journal of Caring Sciences, 19(3), 268Y273.

Baker, A.R. (2006). Handbook of logistics and distribution management. 3rd ed., London, Kogan Page.

Belvedere, V., Laratro, S., and Villa, S. (2019). Supply Chain Integration in Healthcare sector: what strategies are implemented? working paper presented to EUROMA (European Operations Management Association), annual conference 2019.

Bensa, G., et al. (2010). Misurare la performance della logistica del farmaco: applicazione di una metodologia a due casi studio. Mecosan, 19 (74), 9-25.

Bernstein, et al. (2009). The Effect of Emergency Department Crowding on Clinically Oriented Outcomes. Acad Emerg Med. 16 (1):1-10. https://-doi.org/10.1111.

Bodega, D. (2002). Le forme della Leadership. Milano, Etas Libri.

Bohmer, R., and Winslow, A. (1999). The Dana-Farber Cancer Institute, Harvard Business School Case 606-044, July 1999, Boston, MA.

Bohmer, R, and Ferlins, E. (2005). Virginia Mason Medical Center. Harvard Business School Case 606-044, October 2005, Boston, MA.

Borgonovi, E. (1996). Principi e sistemi aziendali per le amministrazioni pubbliche, Milano, Egea.

Borgonovi, E. (2001). Il concetto di valore pubblico. Azienda Pubblica, 2 (3), 185-188.

Borgonovi, E. (2005). Principi e sistemi aziendali per le amministrazioni pubbliche, Milano, Egea.

Boulding, K. (1956). General systems theory – the skeleton of science. Management Science, 2(3), 197.

Boyne, G., (2002). Public and private management: what's the difference? Journal of Management Studies, 39 (1), 97-122.

Bowersox, DJ, and Closs, DJ (1996). Logistical management: the integrated supply chain, London, McGraw Hill.

Bowman, E., and Fetter, R. (1957). Analysis of Production and Operations Management.

Bozarth, C.C. (1993), A Conceptual Model of Manufacturing Focus, International Journal of Operations & Production Management, Vol. 13, N. 1, 81-92.

Bozeman, B., and Kingsley, G. (1998). Risk culture in public and private organizations. Public Administration Review, 58 (2), 109-18.

Bredenhoff, et al. (2010). Exploring types of focused factories in hospital care: a multiple case study. BMC Health Service Research, Vol. 10, N. 154.

Brusoni, M., and Marsilio, M. (2007). La gestione centralizzata degli approvvigionamenti nei sistemi sanitari regionali. In: E. Anessi Pessina, and E. Cantù, eds. Rapporto OASI 2007, Milano, Egea, 373-408.

Bucci, et al. (2016). Emergency Department crowding and hospital bed shortage: is Lean a smart answer? A systematic review European Review for Medical and Pharmacological Sciences 20: 4209-4219.

Burns, et al. (2017). Contributing Factors of Frequent Use of the Emergency Department: A Synthesis. 35 (November): 51-55.

Butow, P., et al. (2015). Clinical pathway for the screening, assessment and management of anxiety and depression in adult cancer patients: Australian guidelines. Psycho-Oncology, Vol. 24, 987-1001.

Callender, G., and McGuire, J. (2007). People in public procurement. In: L. Knight, et al., eds. Public procurement: international cases and commentary, London, Routledge, 314-324.

Capkun V., Messner, M., and Rissbacher, C. (2012), Service specialization and operational performance in hospitals. International Journal of Operations & Production Management, Vol. 32, N. 4, 468-495.

Cardoso, et al. (2011). Impact of Delayed Admission to Intensive Care Units on Mortality of Critically Ill Patients: A Cohort Study. Critical Care2011 15 (R28). https://doi.org/10.1186.

Carey, et al. (2008). Specialty and Full-Service Hospitals: A Comparative Cost Analysis. Health Services Research, Vol. 5, N. 2, 1869-1887.

Centauri, F., Mazzocato, P., Villa, S., and Marsilio, M. (2018). System-wide lean implementation in health care: A multiple case study. Health Services Management Research Vol. 31(2) 60-73.

Chase, R.B., Jacobs, R.F., Aquilano, N.J., Grando, A., and Sianesi, A. (2004). Operations Management nella produzione e nei servizi, Milano, McGraw-Hill.

Chase, R.B., Jacobs R.F. and Aquiliano N.J. (2006) Operations management for competitive advantage, 11 ed., New York, McGraw-Hill.

Chen, D.Q., Preston, D.S., and Xia, W. (2013. Enhancing hospital supply chain performance: A relational view and empirical test. JOM, Vol. 31, 391-408.

Chopra, S., and Meindel, P. (2007). Supply chain management – strategy, planning & operations. 3rd ed., Vol. 1, Englewood Cliffs, NJ: Pearson Prentice-Hall.

Christopher, M. (1992). Logistics: The strategic issues, London, Chapman & Hall.

Colombo, L., and Mauri, M. (2010). Realizzare un ospedale per il XXI secolo. In L'ospedale tra presente e futuro Lega F., Mauri M., Prenestini A. (a cura di), Milano, Egea.

Cook, D., at al. (2014). From 'Solution Shop' Model To 'Focused Factory' In Hospital Surgery: Increasing Care Value and Predictability. Health Affairs, Vol. 33, N. 5, 746-755.

Cooper, M.C., et al. (1997). Supply Chain Management: more than a new name for logistics. The International Journal of Logistics Management, Vol. 8, N. 1, 1-14.

Cox, A., Chicksand, D., and Ireland, P. (2005). Suboptimally in NHS sourcing in the UK: demand-side constraints on supply-side improvement. Public Administration, 83 (2), 367-392.

Crook, T.R., and Combs, J.G., (2007). Sources and consequences of bargaining power in supply chains. Journal of Operations Management, Vol. 25, N. 2, 546-555.

Cunningham, et al. (2006). What Accounts For Differences In The Use Of Hospital Emergency Departments Across U.S. Communities?. Health Affairs, July, 324-36.

Dabhilkar, M., Svarts, A. (2019). From general to specialty hospitals: operationalizing focus in healthcare operations. Operations Management Research, Vol. 12, 94-111.

Davis, M., an Heineke, J. (2005). Operations management, London, McGraw-Hill Irwin.

De Belvis, et al. (2016). Emergency Department Crowding and Hospital Bed Shortage: Is Lean a Smart Answer? A Systematic Review, 20(20) (October): 4209-19.

De Pietro, C., Benvenuti, C., an Sartirana, M. (2011). Gli ospedali per intensità di cura in Toscana: un'esperienza in corso. L'aziendalizzazione della sanità in Italia. Rapporto Oasi; 1:413-34.

De Vries, G., Bertrand, J., an Vissers, J. (1999). Design requirements for health care production control systems. Production. Planning & Control 1999; 10(6):559-69.

Del Vecchio, M., and Rossi, A. (2004). Consorzi di Area Vasta in Toscana: il caso del CAVC tra innovazione gestionale e trasformazione istituzionale. In: E. Anessi Pessina, and E. Cantù, eds. Rapporto OASI 2004. Milano: Egea, 319-347.

Dimitri, N., Dini, F., and Piga, G. (2006). When should procurement be centralized? In: N. Dimitri, G. Piga, and G. Spagnolo, eds. Handbook of procurement, Cambridge, Cambridge University Press, 47-81.

Ding, X. (2015). The impact of service design and process management on clinical quality: An exploration of synergetic effects, JOM, Vol. 36, 103-114.

Doerner, K.F. and Reiman, M., 2007. Logistics of health care management. Computes & Operations Research, 34 (3), 621-623.

Dunleavy, and Hood (1994). From old public administration to new public management. Public Money & Management, Vol. 14, Issue 3, 9-16.

Eastaugh, S.R., (2014). Hospital Specialization: Benefits-Focused Product Line Planning. Healthcare Finance, Vol. 41, N. 3.

Farnham, D., and Horton, S., eds. (1996). Managing the new public services, London, MacMillan.

Fawcett, S.E., Magnan, G.D., McCarter, M.W. (2008). Benefits, barriers, and bridges to effective supply chain management. Supply Chain Management: An International Journal, Vol. 13, N. 1, 35-48.

Fillingham, D. (2008). Lean Healthcare, Kingsham Press.

Fitzgerald, L., Ferlie, E., Wood, M., and Hawkins, C. (2002). Interlocking interactions, the diffusion of innovations in health care. Human Relations, 55(12), 1429.

Fleissig, A., Jenkins, V., Catt, S., Fallowfield, L. (2006). Multidisciplinary teams in cancer care: are they effective in the UK?. Lancet Oncol.; 7: 935-943.

Flynn, N. (2007). Public sector management. 5th ed. London. Sage.

Forster, A.J., Stiell, I., Wells, G., Lee, A.J., and Van Warlaven, C. (2003). The effect of hospital occupancy on emergency department length of stay and patient disposition. Academic Emergency Medicine 2003; 10(2): 127-33.

Freidson, E. (1985). The reorganisation of the medical profession. Medical Care Review, 42 (1), 11-35.

Freidson, E. (1988). Profession of medicine: a study of the sociology of applied knowledge, Chicago, University of Chicago Press.

Friebel, R., Fisher, R., Deeny, S.R., Gardner, T., and Molloy, A. (2019). The implications of high bed occupanct rates on readmissions rates in England: a longitudinal study. Health Policy 123: 765-772.

Friedland, P.L., et al. (2011). Impact of multidisciplinary team management in head and neck cancer patients. British Journal of Cancer, Vol. 104, 1246-1248.

Fulop, N.J., Ramsay, A.I.G. (2019). How organisations contribute to improving the quality of healthcare, BMJ, Vol., N. 1773.

Gabutti, I., Cicchetti, A., and Mascia, D. (2017). Exploring "patient-centered" hospitals: a systematic review to understand change. BMC Health Services Research, 17, 364.

Ganeshan, R., and Harrison, T.P. (1995). An introduction to supply chain management. Report, Department of Management Sciences and Information Systems, Penn State University.

Gawande, A. (2007). Better. A Surgeon's notes on performance, New York, Picador.

Gelderman, C., Ghijsen, P., and Brugman, M. (2006). Public procurement and EU tendering directives – explaining non-compliance. International Journal of Public Sector Management, 19 (7), 702-714.

George, et al. (2006). Effect of Population Ageing on Emergency Department Speed and Efficiency: A Historical Perspective from a District General Hospital in the UK. Emerg Med J 23: 379.

Giangrande, P., Calizzani, G., et. al. (2014). The european standards of Haemophilia centres. Blood transfuse, 12 Suppl 3, s525-30.

Ginsburg, P.B. (2000). Are focused factory the wave of the future?. Frontiers in Health Service Management, Vol. 16, N.3.

Goienetxea, et al. (2017). How Can Decision Makers Be Supported in the Improvement of an Emergency Department? A Simulation, Optimization and Data Mining Approach. Elsevier 15 (December): 102-22.

Gowen III, C.R., and Tallon, W.J. (2003). Enhancing supply chain practices through human resource management. Journal of Management Development, 22 (1), 32-33.

Grando, Verona, and Vicari (2010). Tecnologia, innovazione, operations, Milano, Egea.

Green, L.V., Giulio, J., Green, R., and Soares, J. (2005). Using queueing theory to increase the effectiveness of physicians staffing in the Emergency department Academic Emergency Medicine.

Green, L. (2006). Queuing analysis in healthcare. In Hall, R.W. Patient Flow: Reducing Delay in Healthcare Delivery, Los Angele,s Springer's International Series.

Green, L. (2011). Queueing Theory and Modeling. In Handbook of Healthcare Delivery Systems, London, Ed. Yuehwern Yih.

Hackman, S.T., et al., (2001). Benchmarking warehousing and distribution operations: an input-output approach. Journal of Productivity Analysis, 16 (1), 79-100.

Haraden, C., and Resar, R. (2004). Patient flow in hospitals: understanding and controlling it better. Frontiers of Health Services Management, 20 (4), 3-15.

Harland, C., et al. (2007). Challenges facing public procurement. In: L. Knight, C. Harland, J. Telgen, K. Thai, G. Callender, and K. McKen, eds. Public procurement: international cases and commentary, London, Routledge, 351-357.

Harrison, M., Paez, K., Carman, K., Stephens, J., Smeeding, L., Devers, K., and Garfinkel, S. (2016). Effects of organizational context on lean implementation in five hospital systems. Health Care Management Review, Vol. 41 No. 2, 127-144.

Hendrich, A., Chow, M.P., Skierczynski, B.A., and Lu, Z. (2008). A 36-hospital time and motion study: How do medical-surgical nurses spend their time? Permanente J. 12(3): 25-34.

Herzlinger (1997). Market Drive Healthcare, who wins, who loses in the transformation of Americas largest service industry, Addisson-Wesley publishing company.

Hyer, N.L., et al. (2009). Performance analysis of a focused hospital unit: The case of an integrated trauma center. Journal of Operations Management, Vol. 27, 203-219.

Huckman, R.S., and Zinner, D.E. (2008). Does focus improve operational excellence? Lessons from the management of clinical trials. Strategic Management Journal, Vol. 29, No. 2, 73-93.

Jamison, R.N., Rudy, T.E., Penzien, D.B., and Mosely, T.H.J. (1994). Cognitive-behavioral classifications of chronic pain: replication and extension of empirically derived patient profiles. Pain, Vol. 57, no. 3, 1994.

Jarret, P.G. (1998). Logistics in the health care industry. International Journal of Physical Distribution and Logistics, 28 (9/10), 741-772.

Jarret, P.G. (2006). An analysis of International health care logistics. Leadership in Health Services, 19 (1), i-x.

Kim, S., Horowitz, I., Young, K.K., and Buckley, T.A. (1999). Analysis of capacity management of the intensive care unit in a hospital. European Journal of Operational Research 115: 36-46.

Kowolski, C. (2005). Technology strategy for supply chain management. Healthcare Purchasing News, December 2005, 56.

Kucukyazici, B., Verter, V., and Mayo, N. (2011). An Analytical Framework for Designining Community-Based Care for Chronic Diseases. Production and Operations Management, 20: 3.

Kumar, S. (2010). Specialty hospitals emulating focused factories:A case study. International Journal of Health Care Quality Assurance, Vol. 23 No. 1, 94-109.

Laratro, S., and Villa, S. (2020). Evolution of patient-centered care models: the role of focused hospital, presented to the annual conference of EUROMA, European Operations Management Association.

Lega, F., DePietro, C. (2005). Converging patterns in hospital organization: beyond the professional bureaucracy. Health Policy 74: 261-281.

Lega, F., Marsilio, M., and Villa, S. (2013). An evaluation framework for measuring supply chain performance in the public healthcare sector: evidence from the Italian NHS. Production, Planning and Control Volume 24 Issue 10-11, 931-947.

Legramante, J.M., Morciano, L., Lucaroni, F., Gilardi, F., Credda, E., Pesaresi, A., et al. (2016). Frequent Use of Emergency Departments by the Elderly Population When Continuing Care is Not Well Established. PLOSONE, DOI:10.1371/journal.pone.0165939December14,201.

Litvak, E., and Long, M.C. (2000). Cost and quality under managed care: irreconcilable differences? The American Journal of Managed Care, 6 (3), 305-312.

Litvak, E., Buerhaus, P., Davidoff, F., Long, M., McManus, M., and Berwick, D. (2005). Managing unnecessary variability in patient demand to reduce nursing stress and improve patient safety. Journal on Quality and Patient Safety, 31(6):330-8.

Litvak, E., and Bisognano, M. (2011). More patients, less payment: increasing hospital efficiency in the aftermath of health reform. Health Affairs; 30(1):76-80.

Marsilio, M., and Mele, S. (2010). La centralizzazione degli acquisti in sanità: esperienze internazionali a confronto. Mecosan, 19 (75), 3-23.

Marsilio, M., Torbica, A., and Villa, S. (2017). Healthcare Multidisciplinary Teams: The Sociotechnical approach for an integrated system-wide perspective. Health Care Management Review 42 (4): 315-327, October/December.

Marsilio, M., Salmasi, L., Tomas Roldan, E., and Villa, S. (2020). Redesigning Emergency Department Patient Flows: evidence from an Italian benchmarking study working paper presented to the annual conference of EUROMA, European Operations Management Association

Martone, R.F. (2007). La produzione nelle aziende di servizi pubblici. Aspetti teorici ed operativi, Padova, Cedam.

Mattison, Melissa (2019). Hospital Management of older adults. UpToDate.

Mazzocato, P. (2007). Applying operations management methods to health care delivery, (Stockolm: Karolinska Institutet).

Mazzocato, P., Savage, C., Brommels, M., Aronsson, H., and Thor, J. (2010). Lean thinking in healthcare: A realist review of the literature. Quality & Safety in Health Care, 19(5), 376-382.

McDermott, C.M., and Stock, G.N. (2011). Focus as emphasis: Conceptual and performance implications for hospitals. Journal of Operations Management, Vol. 29, 616-626.

McDermott, C.M., and Stock, G.N. (2011). Focus as emphasis: Conceptual and performance implications for hospitals. Journal of Operations Management, Vol. 29, 616-626.

McKone-Sweet, K.E., Hamilton, P., and Willis, S.B. (2005). The ailing healthcare supply chain: a prescription for change. Journal of Supply Chain Management, 41 (1), 4-17.

McLaughlin, D., Yang, S., and van Dierdonck. R. (1995). Professional service organizations and focus. Management Science, Vol. 41, 1185-1193.

McLaughlin, D. (1996). Why variation reduction is not everything: a new paradigm for service operations. International Journal of Service Industry Management, Vol. 7 No. 3 17-30.

McLaughlin, D., and Hays, J. (2008). Healthcare Operations Management, Health Administration Press, Chicago, USA.

Malkin-Washeim, D.L., Dapkins, I., and Huggins, C.E. (2017). Multidisciplinary Team Visits Offer Unique Approach in the Bronx. AADE in Practice, 5(2), 2430.

Mant, J. (2001). Process versus outcome indicators in the assessment of quality of health care. International Journal for Quality in Health Care, Vol. 13, N. 6, 475-480.

Marsilio, M., Torbica, A., and Villa, S. (2017). Healthcare Multidisciplinary Teams: The Sociotechnical approach for an integrated system-wide perspective. Health Care Management Review, 42 (4): 315-327, October/December.

Mitchell, R., Parker, V., Giles, M., Boyle, B. (2014). The ABC of health care team dynamics: understanding complex affective, behavioral, and cognitive dynamics in interprofessional teams. Health Care Management Review., Vol. 39, N. 1, 1-9.

Moore, M. (1997). Creating Public Value: Strategic Management in Government, Cambridge, Massachusetts, USA, Harvard University Press.

Moore, M. (2000). Managing for value: organizational strategy in For-Profit, Non Profit, and Governmental Organizations. Nonprofit and Voluntary Sector Quarterly, 29 (1), 183-204.

Morotti, G., et al. (2006). La logistica a supporto dei servizi sanitari nell'Area Vasta toscana. Modelli gestionali e possibili sviluppi. Organizzazione Sanitaria, 30 (4), 5-15.

Morris, et al. (2012). Emergency Department Crowding: Towards an Agenda for Evidence-Based Intervention. Emerg Med J 29: 460-66. https://doi.org/10.1136/emj.2010.107078.

Moschuri, S.J., and Kondylis, M.N. (2006). Outsourcing in public hospitals: a Greek perspective. Journal of Health Organization and Management, 20 (1), 4-14.

Nancarrow, S.A., Booth, A., Ariss, S., Smith, T., Enderby, P., and Roots, A. (2013). Ten principles of good interdisciplinary team work. Human Resources for Health, 11, 19.

Newell, T.L., Steinmetz-Malato, L.L., and Van Dyke, D.L. (2011). Applying Toyota production system techniques for medication delivery: improving hospital safety and efficiency. Journal for Healthcare Quality, Vol. 33 No. 2, 15-22.

Nicholson, L., Vakharia, A.J., and Erenguc, S.S. (2004). Outsourcing inventory management decisions in healthcare: models and application. European Journal of Operational Research, 154 (1), 271-290.

Nicosia, F. (2010). L'ospedale snello. Tecniche lean in sanità, Milano, Franco Angeli.

Noon, C.E., Hankins, C.T., and Coté, M.J. (2003). Understanding the impact of variation in the delivery of healthcare services. Journal of Healthcare Management, 48 (2), 82-97.

Norris, H. (1988). Remaining competitive by controlling delivered costs. Hospital Material Management Quarterly, 9 (3), 57-72.

Orlandi, W, Duca, E, and Pioppo, M. (2006). L'ospedale per aree di intensità di cura omogenee e di assistenza multispecialistica: l'esperienza dell'Azienda usl n. 3 dell'Umbria. Organizzazione Sanitaria. (2006):35-40.

Pagliantini, S., Nerattini, M., and Tomassini, C. (2009). La logistica del paziente nel percorso dell'emergenza urgenza: il caso della Dicharge Room senese. Mecosan Vol. 18 70: 23-44.

Parenti, et al. (2010). Reliability and Validity of an Italian Four-Level Emergency Triage System. Emerg Med. J. 27 (June): 495-98. https://doi.org/10.1136/emj.2008.070193.

Peltokorpi, A. et al. (2016). Five focus strategies to organize health care delivery. International Journal of Health Care Quality Assurance, Vol. 29, N. 2, 177-191.

Perera, et al. (2014). Clearing emergency departments and clogging war ds: National Emergency Access Target and the law of unintended consequences Emergency Medicine Australasia 26, 549-555.

Pieters, A., et al. (2010). No cure for all evils: Dutch obstetric care and limits to the applicability of the focused factory concept in health care. International Journal of Operations & Production Management, Vol. 30, N. 11, 1112-1139.

Pillay B. et al. (2016). The impact of multidisciplinary team meetings on patient assessment, management and outcomes in oncology settings: A systematic review of the literature. Cancer Treatment Review, Vol. 42, 56-72.

Po, J., Rundall, T.G., Shortell, S.M., and Blodgett, J.C. (2019). Lean Management and U.S. Public Hospital Performance: Results From a National Survey. Journal of Healthcare Management, Vol. 64 No. 6, 363-379.

Porter, M. (2008). Value-Based Health Care Delivery. Annals of Surgery, Vol. 248, N. 4, October 2008.

Poulin, E. (2003). Benchmarking the hospital logistics process: a potential cure for the ailing healthcare sector. CMA Management, 77 (1), 20-24.

Power, D., (2005). Supply Chain Management integration and implementation: a literature review. Supply Chain Management: an international journal, Vol. 10, N. 4, 252-263.

Radnor, Z., et al., (2006). Evaluation of the lean approach to business management and its use in the public sector, Edinburgh, Scottish Executive.

Radnor, Z., et al. (2016). Public Service Operations Management: A research handbook Taylor and Francis.

Rafiq, M., et al. (2019). Extreme Consumers of Health Care: Patterns of Care Utilization in Patients with Multiple Chronic Conditions Admitted to a Novel Integrated Clinic. Journal of Multidisciplinary Healthcare, Vol. 12, 1075-1083.

Richardson, et al. (2009). Myths versus Facts in Emergency Department Overcrowding and Hospital Access Block. The Medical Journal of Australia 190 (7): 369-74. https://doi.org/10.5694.

Riopel, D., Langevin, A., and Campbell, J.F. (2005). The network of logistics decisions. In: A. Langevin, and D. Riopel, eds. Logistics system: definition and optimization, New York, Springer, 1-38.

Schotanus, F., and Telgen, J. (2007). Developing a typology of organizational forms of cooperative Purchasing. Journal of Purchasing and Supply Management, 13 (1), 53-68.

Shortell, S.M., Blodgett, J.C., Rundall, T.G., and Kralovec, P. (2018). Use of Lean and related transformational performance improvement systems in hospitals in the United States: Results from a national survey. Joint Commission Journal on Quality and Patient Safety, Vol. 44 No. 10, 574-582.

Skinner W. (1974). The focused factory. Harvard Business Review, Vol. 52, N. 3, 113-122.

Stadler,H. (2008). Supply chain management – an overview. In: Stadler, H., and Kilger, C., eds. Supply chain management and advanced planning: concepts, models, software and case studies, Berlin, Springer, 9-33.

Stephens, M.R., et al. (2006). Multidisciplinary team management is associated with improved outcomes after surgery for esophageal cancer. Diseases of the Esophagus, Vol. 19, Issue 3, 164-171.

Sugarhood, P., Wherton, J., Procter, R., Hinder, S., and Greenhalgh, T. (2014). Technology as system innovation: A key informant interview study of the application of the diffusion of innovation model to telecare. Disability and Rehabilitation. Assistive Technology, 9(1), 79-87.

Suter, E., Oelke, N.D., Adair, C.E., and Armitage,G.D. (2009). Ten key principles for successful health systems integration. Healthc Q, Vol. 13, 16-23, 2009.

Terwiesch, C. (2011). The Effects of Focus on Performance: Evidence from California Hospitals, Management Science. Vol. 57, N. 11, 1897-1912.

Tomassini, C.R. (2019). Liste di attesa in sanità. La soluzione dell'Open Access, Roma, Il Pensiero Scientifico Editore.

Tozzi, V. (2004). La gestione per processi in sanità, Mecosan, n. 50.

Turk, D.C., and Rudy, T.E. (1988). Toward an empirically derived taxonomy of chronic pain patients: Integration of psychological assessment data. Journal of Consulting and Clinical Psychology, Vol. 56, no. 2.

Van Dijk, C.E., Hoekstra, T., Verheij, R.A., et al. (2013). Type II diabetes patients in primary care: profiles of healthcare utilization obtained from observational data, BMC Health Serv Res, Vol. 13, N. 7.

Vermeulen, M.J., Ray, J., Bell, C., Cayen, B., Stuckel T.A., and Schull, M.J. (2009). Disequilibrium between admitted and discharged hospitalized patients affects emergency department length of stay. Annals of Emergency Medicine 2009; 54(6): 794-804.

Villa, S., Barbieri, M., and Lega, F. (2009). Restructuring patient flow logistics around patient care needs: implications and practicalities from three critical cases. Health Care Management Science, 12:155-165.

Villa, S. (2012). L'operations management a supporto del sistema di operazioni aziendali. Modelli di analisi e soluzioni progettuali per il settore sanitario, Padova, Cedam.

Villa, S., Prenestini, A., and Giusepi, I. (2014). A framework to analyze hospital-wide patient flow logistics: Evidence from an Italian comparative study. Health Policy, 115: 196-205.

Villa, S., Basso, M., Chiappa, L., Cimino, E., De Cristofaro, R., Di Minno, G., D'Onofrio, G., Giubbini, G., Laratro, S., Mancuso, E., Sacco, P., Peyvandi, F., Santagostino, E., Tomas Roldan E., and De Belvis, A.G. (2020). Costruzione di percorsi clinico organizzativi per una migliore presa in carico del paziente emofilico: quali insegnamenti per la gestione della cronicità, in Report Annuale OMAR (Osservatorio MAlattie Rare).

Vissers, J. (1998). Patient flow-based allocation of inpatient resources: a case study. European Journal of Operational Research, 105 (2), 356-370.

Vissers, J., and Beech, R. (2005). Health Operations Management, New York, Routledge Health Management Series.

Vissers, J., and De Vries, G. (2011). A framework for production control in health care organizations. Production, Planning and Control 2001; 12(6): 591-604.

Vliet Vlieland, T.P.M. (2004). Multidisciplinary team care and outcomes in rheumatoid arthritis. Current Opinion in Rheumatology, Vol. 16, Issue 2, 153-156.

Vogeli, C., Shields, A.E., Lee, T.A., et al. (2007). Multiple chronic conditions: prevalence, health consequences, and implications for quality, care management, and costs. J Gen Intern Med. 2007; 22 Suppl 3(Suppl 3): 391-395. doi: 10.1007/s11606-007-0322-1.

Von Bertalanffy, L. (1969). General system theory: Foundations, development, applications, New York, George Braziller Inc.

Vokurka, R.J., and Davis, R.A. (2000). Focused Factories: empirical study of structural and performance differences, Production and Inventory Management Journal, Vol. 41, N. 1.

Walley, P., and Steyn, R. (2006). Managing Variation in Demand: lessons from the UK National Health Service. Journal of Healthcare Management, 51 (5), 309-322.

Wang, et al. (2018). Causes of Emergency Department Overcrowding and Blockage of Access to Critical Services in Beijing: A 2-Year Study. The Journal of Emergency Medicine 54 (5): 665-67E3.

Westwood, N., James-Moore, M., and Cooke, M. (2007). Going Lean in the NHS. NHS Institute for Innovation and Improvement, UK.

Yarmohammadian, et al. (2017). Overcrowding in Emergency Departments: A Review of Strategies to Decrease Future Challenges. J Res Med Sci 22 (23). https://doi.org/10.4103/1735-1995.200277.

Zanjirani, R., Farahani, N., and Davarzani, H. (2009). Supply chain and logistics in national, international and government environment, Heidelberg, Physica-Verlag Springer.